Systematics and classification

Grace Monger and Mary Sangster

Revised Nuffield Advanced Science
Published for the Nuffield–Chelsea Curriculum Trust
by Longman Group UK Limited

Longman Group UK Limited
Longman House, Burnt Mill, Harlow,
Essex CM20 2JE, England
and associated companies throughout the World

Set in Monophoto Times Roman (327) and
Univers Medium Condensed (690)

Produced by Longman Group (Far East) Limited
Printed in Hong Kong

ISBN 0 582 35436 6

The authors would like to acknowledge with thanks the helpful
advice of Dr Peter L. Forey and Dr Geoffrey Harper on the
systematics section, and that of Dr M. Hudson, Dr David J.
Patterson, and Professor P.H.A. Sneath on the classification section.

Contents

Acknowledgements

Photographs

AFRC Institute of Food Research, Norwich: figure 33.

Heather Angel: figures 39/1, 55, 68/1, 68/3, 70/1, 75/1, 75/3, 75/4, 75/9, 88/5, 91, 103, 117/3, 117/4, 117/7, 118/1, 118/4, 118/5, 119/5, 121/3, 121/4, 130/6.

Ardea London Ltd: J. P. Ferrero: figure 131/5.

Dr. M. J. Bibb and Dr. J. Burgess, Department of Genetics, John Innes Institute, Norwich: figures 44/2, 44/3.

Biophoto Associates: figures: 4, 9a, 9b, 31/2, 36/2, 46, 51, 52, 57, 59, 61, 62, 63, 65, 68/2, 74/1, 74/2, 79, 80/2, 81, 82, 83/1, 83/3, 83/6, 84, 88/3, 89, 96/1, 106/1, 110/1, 117/1, 119/2, 121/2, 123, 129/2, 130/5.

The Bridgeman Art Library: cover
Bruce Coleman Ltd: Erwin & Peggy Bauer: figure 131/2; Jane Burton: figures 97, 109, 113/2, 115, 121/5, 128/1, 128/4, 131/4; Bruce Coleman: figure 130/2; Eric Crichton: figures 67/1, 67/3, 67/4, 71/2, 72/1, 75/2; Wayne Lankinen: figure 131/3; R. K. Murton: figure 85/1; Allan Power: figures 98/1, 121/1, 126; Prato: figure 88/1; Hans Reinhard: figures 67/2, 75/6, 88/4; Frieder Sauer: figure 100; Walter Schmidt: figure 83/5; Nancy Sefton: figures 93, 98/3; M. Γ. Soper: figure 117/5; Kim Taylor: figures 117/2, 117/6, 131/1; G. Ziesler: figure 129/4.

Guy Cox and Teresa Dibbayawan, Electron Microscope Unit, University of Sydney: figure 37.

Professor J. D. Dodge, Department of Botany, Royal Holloway and Bedford New College, University of London: figures 47/1, 47/2.

Dr. C. S. Dow, Department of Biological Sciences, University of Warwick: figure 35.

Electron Microscopy Research Group, Clinical Research Centre, Harrow, Middlesex: figure 30.

Dr. D. S. Ellis, Electron Microscopy Laboratory, London School of Hygiene and Tropical Medicine: figures 43/1, 43/2, 60, 64/2.

Philip Harris Biological Ltd: figure 85/2.

Eric and David Hosking: John Hawkins: figure 130/1; David Hosking: figure 125; Eric Hosking: figures 129/3, 130/7; Dr. D. P. Wilson: figures 48, 96/2, 98/2, 111/1, 127.

Imperial Chemical Industries plc, Plant Protection Division – Fernhurst: figure 40/2.

Institute of Horticultural Research: 75/5, 75/8.

Dr. Tobias Kieser, Department of Genetics, John Innes Institute, Norwich: figure 44/1.

Frank Lane Picture Agency Ltd: Chris Newton: figure 128/2.

London Scientific Films Ltd: figures 64/1, 76, 105.

The National Collections of Industrial and Marine Bacteria Ltd, Torry Research Station, Aberdeen: figure 45.

Natural History Photographic Agency: J. & M. Bain: figure 53; A. Bannister: figure 71/1; H. Canter-Lund: figure 36/1; S. Dalton: figure 128/3; K. Ghani: figure 75/7; B. Hawkes: figure 83/4; E. A. Janes: figure 88/2; L. Lemoine: figure 118/2; M. Walker: figure 107.

Oxford Scientific Films Ltd: Doug Allen: figure 130/3; G. I. Bernard: figure 124; J. A. L. Cooke: figures 118/3, 119/4; Michael Fogden: figure 129/1; R. Templeton: figure 130/4; David Thompson: figure 114; P. & W. Ward: figure 119/3; Peter Ward: figure 119/1.

Dr. D. J. Patterson, Department of Zoology, University of Bristol: figures 49, 56.

Professor J. R. Postgate: figure 34.

Dr. M. C. F. Proctor, Department of Biological Sciences, University of Exeter: figures 87, 90/2.

Promotion Australia: figure 131/6.

Dr. Alan Radford, Department of Genetics, University of Leeds: figure 83/2.

Science Photo Library: Dr. Tony Brain: figure 40/1; Dr. Jeremy Burgess: figure 39/2; Dr. Rosalind King: figure 32.

Dr. J. D. Thomas, School of Biological Sciences, University of Sussex: figure 110/2.

The translation on page 9 is from: Wentworth Thompson, D'A. *Historia animalium*. Vol. IV, from *The Works of Aristotle* Eds. Smith, J. A. and Ross, W. D. Clarendon Press, 1970.

Dr. C. W. Wells, Department of Histopathology, St. Bartholomew's Hospital, London: figures 31/1, 42.

Artwork and tables

Ayala, F. J. 'The mechanisms of evolution'. Copyright © 1978 by *Scientific American*, Inc. All rights reserved: figure 23.

Barnes, R. D. *Invertebrate zoology*. Saunders, 4th edition 1980: figures 108, 113/1, Table 13.

Bendich, A. J. and McCarthy, B. J. 'DNA comparisons among barley, oats, rye and wheat'. *Genetics.* **65**. 1970. 545–565: figures 21, 22.

Buchsbaum, R. *Animals without backbones*. Pelican, Revised edition 1964. Reprinted by permission of Penguin Books Ltd: figures 92, 102, 120.

Butcher, R. W. *A new illustrated British flora*. Leonard Hill, 1961: figure 5c.

Christiansen, M. S. *Grasses, sedges and rushes in colour*. Blandford Press, 1979: figure 10b.

Fairbrothers, D. E. in Heywood, V. H. (Ed.) *Modern methods in plant taxonomy*. Academic Press, 1967: figure 19.

Feldman, M. and Sears, E. R. 'The wild gene resources of wheat'. Copyright © 1981 by *Scientific American*, Inc. All rights reserved: figure 25.

Haeckel, E. *Generelle Morphologie der Organismen*. Georg Reimer, Berlin, 1866: figure 6.

Hanson, E. D. *Animal diversity*. © 1964. Reprinted by permission of Prentice-Hall, Englewood Cliffs, New Jersey: figure 7.

Hill, L. R. in Gibbs, B. M. and Shapton, D. A. (Eds) *Identification methods for microbiologists*. Part B. Academic Press, 1968: figure 15.

Hubbard, C. E. *Grasses*. Pelican, 1968. Reprinted by permission of Penguin Books Ltd: figure 10.

Kirk, D. L. *Biology today*. Random House, 1972: figures 66, 70/2, 72/2, 73, 80/1, 86, 92, 94, 116.

Kohne, D. E. in Hawkes, J. G. (Ed.) *Chemotaxonomy and serotaxonomy*. Academic Press, 1967: figure 20.

Margulis, L. and Schwartz, K. V. *Five Kingdoms – an illustrated guide to the phyla of Life on Earth*. W. H. Freeman, 1982: figures 38, 41, 50, 71/3, 77, 106/2, Tables 11, 14.

Raven, P. H., Evert, R. F., and Curtis, H. *Biology of plants*. Worth Publishers, Inc. 3rd edition 1981: figures 54, 58.

Rhodes, F. H. T. *The evolution of Life*. Pelican, 1976. Reprinted by permission of Penguin Books Ltd: figures 2, 8.

Romer, A. S. *The vertebrate body*. W. B. Saunders, 1970: figure 122.

Ross-Craig, S. *Drawings of British plants*. Parts XI and XXIV. Bell & Hyman, 1979: figures 5a and b.

Scagel, R. F. *et al. Evolutionary survey of the Plant Kingdom*. Wadsworth, 1966: figure 90.

Schopf, J. W. 'The evolution of the earliest cells'. Copyright © 1978 by *Scientific American*, Inc. All rights reserved: figure 28.

Smith, P. M. *The chemotaxonomy of plants*. Contemporary Biology series. Edward Arnold, 1976: Table 6.

Stace, C. A. *Plant taxonomy and biosystematics*. Edward Arnold, 1980: figures 1, 18, Tables 2, 10.

Strobel, G. A. and Lanier, G. N. 'Dutch Elm Disease'. Copyright © 1981 by *Scientific American*, Inc. All rights reserved: figure 26.

Systematics

Introduction

Human beings are natural classifiers. Their minds are constantly at work trying to impose order on the enormous variety of phenomena they find in the world around them. Classification is essential to them, for there is too much information input for the human brain to handle unless it is organised into manageable categories. The very act of classifying seems to be a satisfying exercise for humans, whether it is applied to a stamp collection, a library of books, or records of any kind. Once the classification is constructed its usefulness is apparent, as it is simple to add new items in the appropriate place and to retrieve information without having to search the whole collection.

Early attempts to draw up classifications which included all living things were made by philosophers, Aristotle and his followers among them. Ever since then classification has held a central position in biology although, as the oldest biological discipline, it has had periods of popularity and rapid development and periods of stagnation.

A good biological classification must provide a name for each recognizable kind of organism, and identify it precisely, for if biologists all over the world are to be able to communicate facts about an organism, they need to be certain that they are talking about the same one. This classification must also provide groupings which bring together similar organisms and separate those which are different.

The scale of the problem

The scale of the problem presented to a contemporary biologist interested in classifying the living world is enormous. The number of described living species in major groups is approximately 1.5 million. If fossil species are included an estimate of the total number of species which have ever existed could be in the region of 500 million.

No one person can be an expert in all groups, so a good system of classification is essential, which biologists working in all branches of the subject can use. Ecologists for instance, depend heavily on accurate identification of species.

Types of classification

Plants and animals can be classified with a particular purpose in mind. Gardeners have many of these groupings: for example, annuals, biennials, perennials; lime-loving plants, lime-tolerant plants, lime-hating plants. These 'special-purpose' classifications only tell you about one aspect of the plant – the length of its life history or the soil it will grow in. These are important facts for the gardeners to know, but if a plant is labelled 'lime-hating perennial' you cannot predict any other characters it might have or share with other 'lime-hating perennials'.

A classification based on as many different characteristics of organisms as possible is generally much more useful. This is because it enables predictions to be made about the characteristics of any particular organism. For example, if you are told that an animal named *Felis* belongs to the sub-class Eutheria you could make a number of predictions about this animal based on the many 'eutherian' characters used to construct the group originally. You could predict the presence of hair, mammary glands, a spiral cochlea in the inner ear, and two generations of teeth (milk and permanent).

How a system of classification is produced

The science of classification is called *taxonomy*. Taxonomy may be defined as the study of the principles, rules and procedures of classification. Another widely used term is *systematics*. Systematics may be defined as the scientific study of the diversity of living things and of the relationships among them. By these definitions systematics includes taxonomy, but the two words are often used synonymously.

The basic unit of classification is the *species*, the name given to each different 'kind' of organism. A species is usually defined as a group of actually or potentially interbreeding natural populations which is reproductively isolated from other such groups.

Each species is known by a *binomial* (two-word name), for example:

Canis domesticus   dog
Canis lupus   wolf

The first word of the binomial refers to the *genus* (plural genera). A genus is a group of closely related species such as the dog and wolf. The second word distinguishes the species.

The binomial system in use today was established by the Swedish naturalist Linnaeus (see page 10), although a binomial system had often been used in earlier classifications.

Closely related genera are grouped together in one family, related

Figure 1
Two ways of representing how species are organized into groups:
a Dendrogram (elevation).
b 'Box-in-box' (plan).

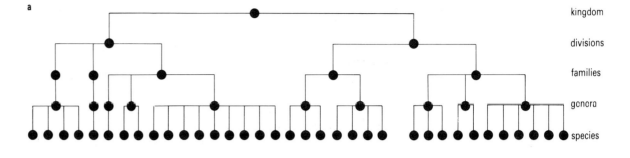

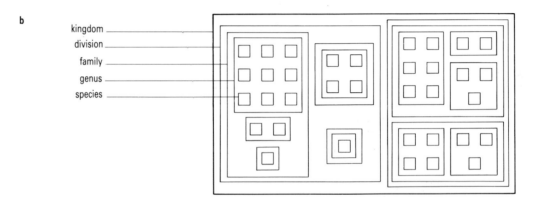

families are grouped into orders and so on. The number of taxonomic ranks which are needed to organize all living things into orderly groups has been decided gradually as taxonomy has developed and more and more species have been described.

This ascending series of successively larger ranks is called a *hierarchy*. Not all taxonomists use the same number of ranks in their hierarchies, but the following will normally be used:

    Kingdom
    Phylum (botanists usually use Division)
    Class
    Order
    Family
    Genus
    Species

Additional levels may be added into the hierarchy by using prefixes, so you can have for example a sub-species or a super-family if necessary.

Figure 1 shows two ways of representing how species may be organized into larger taxonomic groups.

Figure 2 shows how a familiar animal species is classified, and table 1 illustrates the classification of two common plants.

You have now been introduced to the nature of taxonomy and the terms which taxonomists use.

It is very worthwhile to look at collections of plants and animals and to consider the diversity of living things. It should be possible for you to sort out such collections into major groupings on the basis of the characteristics they have in common. If you do try this yourself you may not end up with the exact groups which biologists use, but there should be a resemblance between the two. A classification showing the major groups of living organisms is given in the second section of this book, but you may use any other reference available to you.

The rest of this section is concerned with the historical development of taxonomy, particularly the position it has in contemporary biology and its current usefulness.

Figure 2
A classification of the lion showing the
various taxa from species to kingdom.

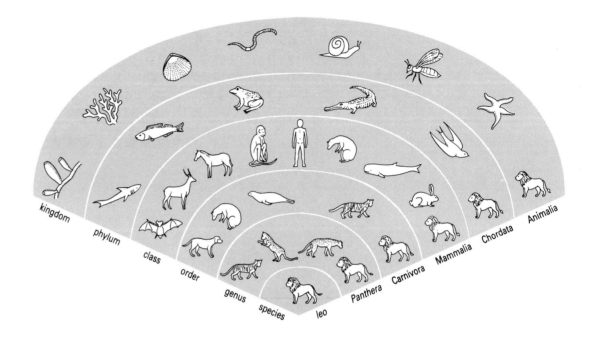

Rank of group	Name of group	
Kingdom	Plant	Plant
Division	Tracheophyta (vascular plants)	Tracheophyta
Sub-division	Spermatophytina (seed-bearing plants)	Spermatophytina
Class	Angiospermopsida (flowering plants, seeds enclosed)	Coniferopsida (seeds not enclosed)
Sub-class	Dicotyledonidae (seeds with two cotyledons or 'seed leaves')	
Order	Ranales	Coniferales
Family	Ranunculaceae	Pinaceae
Genus	*Ranunculus*	*Pinus*
Species	*repens*	*sylvestris*
Common name	Creeping buttercup	Scots pine

Table 1
Classification of the creeping buttercup and Scots pine

The development of taxonomy

The first notable taxonomist was Aristotle (384–322 BC). Besides being a philosopher he studied biology, and as a result of applying his principles of logic to nature he believed that all natural things could be classified into a fixed number of types. All members of a group ('dolphins' for example) would share the essential features of the type and therefore closely resemble one another. This approach meant that individual variation tended to be disregarded and that gaps between the groups were exaggerated.

Aristotle emphasized that all sorts of characters – morphological, embryological, behavioural and ecological – should be compared when classifying organisms. He recognized groups such as 'birds', 'fish' and 'insects', although the fact that he used single, key characteristics like 'terrestrial' or 'aquatic' to separate the groups created problems, which Aristotle himself realized.

The following extracts from his *Historia animalium* ('History of animals') illustrate the sort of characters he used and the problems which they posed. The extracts also give a glimpse of the remarkable knowledge of animals which the Greeks had at that time.

From Book 1:

Of animals that can fly some are furnished with feathered wings, as the eagle and the hawk; some are furnished with membranous wings, as the bee and the cockchafer; others are furnished with leathern wings, as the flying fox and the bat. All flying creatures possessed of blood have feathered wings or leathern wings; the bloodless creatures have membranous wings, as insects. The creatures that have feathered wings or leathern wings have either two feet or no feet at all: for there are said to be certain flying serpents in Ethiopia that are destitute of feet.

Creatures that have feathered wings are classed as a genus under the name of 'bird'; the other two genera, the leathern-winged and membrane-winged, are as yet without a generic title.

Of creatures that can fly and are bloodless some are coleopterous or sheath-winged, for they have their wings in a sheath or shard, like the cockchafer and the dung-beetle; others are sheathless, and of these latter some are dipterous and some tetrapterous: tetrapterous, such as are comparatively large or have their stings in the tail, dipterous, such as are comparatively small or have their stings in front. The coleoptera, are, without exception, devoid of stings; the diptera have the sting in front, as the fly, the horsefly, the gadfly, and the gnat.

From Book 2:

But the dolphin is equipped in the most remarkable way of all animals: the dolphin and other similar aquatic animals, including the other cetaceans which resemble it; that is to say, the whale, and all the other creatures that are furnished with a blow-hole. One can hardly allow that such an animal is terrestrial and terrestrial only, or aquatic and aquatic only, if by terrestrial we mean an animal that inhales air, and if by aquatic we mean an animal that takes in water. For the fact is the dolphin performs both these processes: he takes in water and discharges it by his blow-hole, and he also inhales air into his lungs; for, by the way, the creature is furnished with this organ and respires thereby, and accordingly, when caught in the nets, he is quickly suffocated for lack of air. He can also live for a considerable while out of the water, but all this while he keeps up a dull moaning sound corresponding to the noise made by air-breathing animals in general; furthermore, when sleeping, the animal keeps his nose above water, and he does so that he may breathe the air. Now it would be unreasonable to assign one and the same class of animals to both categories, terrestrial and aquatic, seeing that these categories are more or less exclusive of one another; we must accordingly supplement our definition of the term 'aquatic' or 'marine'. For the fact is, some aquatic animals take in water and discharge it again, for the same reason that leads air-breathing animals to inhale air: in other words, with the object of cooling the blood. Others take in water as incidental to their mode of feeding; for as they get their food in the water they cannot but take in water along with their food, and if they take in water they must be provided with some organ for discharging it. Those blooded animals, then, that use water for a purpose analogous to respiration are provided with gills; and such as take in water when catching their prey, with the blow-hole. Similar remarks are applicable to molluscs and crustaceans; for again it is by way of procuring food that these creatures take in water.

It is not surprising that Aristotle did not produce a completely consistent classification, but his work was important in the history of taxonomy. For almost 2000 years after the death of Aristotle students used a system of classification based on his ideas. It was not until the seventeenth century that any great progress in the study of natural history took place. This was largely the result of explorers and travellers returning to Europe and bringing previously unknown plant and animal specimens with them. A renewed interest in classification followed because there was now a greater diversity of organisms to accommodate.

John Ray (1627–1705) was a remarkable English naturalist who spent his life observing and experimenting with plants and animals in Britain and the rest of Europe. He produced a series of volumes on the classification of plants, birds, fishes, mammals and reptiles, and left an unfinished history of insects.

Ray used a large number of characters in his classifications, and for this reason they were in many ways technically superior to those developed later. The second edition of Ray's *Classification of plants* dealt with 18 000 species which he classified using many characteristics of the flowers and other parts of the plants. His classifications were rather unmanageable, and because of this and the fact that he did not use the binomial system of naming they did not survive. Yet Ray did make a significant contribution to the method of classification, and he is commemorated in the name of the prestigious Ray Society of London which still publishes monographs and papers on classification.

Figure 3

How a Linnaean hierarchy is constructed. The letters A – L represent different taxonomic characters. All members in each circle will exhibit all the characters shown in the circle; and as you move down the hierarchy, the number of characters shared increases.

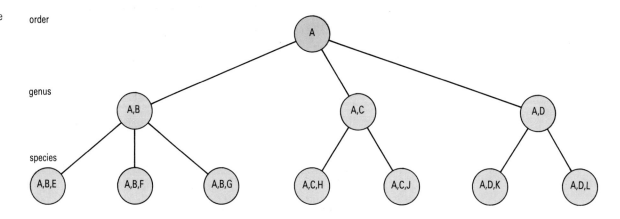

Carolus Linnaeus (1707–1778), the great Swedish naturalist, was the most eminent and influential taxonomist. His two great achievements were a clear system of naming living things, and a system of classification which was simple and logical to use. Linnaeus intended to 'celebrate God's creation' by presenting 'the plan of creation' – that is, a systematic catalogue of all living things.

In the 10th edition of his *Systemae naturae* (1758) Linnaeus, for the first time, consistently applied the clear binomial nomenclature which is still almost universally used. His basic unit was the species. Like Aristotle, he saw a species as a fixed and unchanging entity consisting of a group of organisms which closely resembled a given type. He described each species by a binomial and grouped species into genera, genera into orders, and so on, producing a hierarchy such as that described on page 8. His groupings were on the basis of a 'key' character shared between the members of the group (figure 3). There are problems using this approach, since it gives undue importance or 'weight' to the character used.

The art of classification at that time lay in choosing a suitable key character which would prevent the production of clearly incongruous groups when other characters were compared. In practice, although some of Linnaeus' groups have remained good most have not. For instance, Linnaeus divided flowering plants into 24 classes largely on the basis of the number of stamens they had (figure 4).

The class Diandra ('two stamens') included, among others, three different genera – *Circaea*, *Salvia* and *Anthoxanthum* – which are now placed in entirely separate families – Onagraceae, Lamiaceae and Poaceae, respectively. This is because their two stamens, the key character used, are surrounded by many other features which are not shared (figure 5).

This type of classification where one character is given weight before the classification is made is termed an 'artificial' system. Many of the early classifications were artificial. Their major drawback was that they did not allow other predictions about members of the same group to be made with any degree of certainty.

Linnaean classification was orderly and it appealed to botanists and zoologists, who continued to use it during the nineteenth century when many more species were described and more levels added to the hierarchy. With later adaptations, we still use it today.

Gradually taxonomists sought to group together organisms after comparing many characters rather than choosing a single key character. This method produced more natural groupings and meant that members of a group had more characters which they all possessed. These shared characters were given high 'weight' and became important in constructing 'natural' classifications. Taxonomists began to feel that they had found a natural order in living things. Most existing good classifications are the result of using this method.

In 1859, Darwin in his famous book *On the Origin of Species by means of Natural Selection* suggested that natural taxonomic groups exist because the members have evolved from a common ancestor. Darwin took the classifications in use at the time and showed them to be consistent with his theory of evolution. He proposed that the evolutionary pathways of organisms (called their phylogeny) could explain the order already found in nature and he considered that this

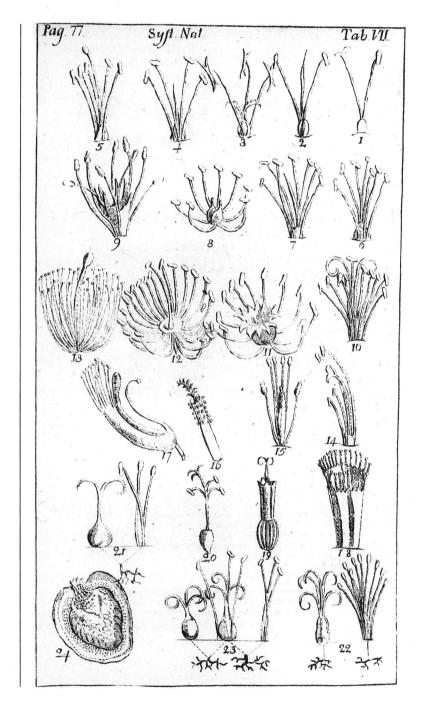

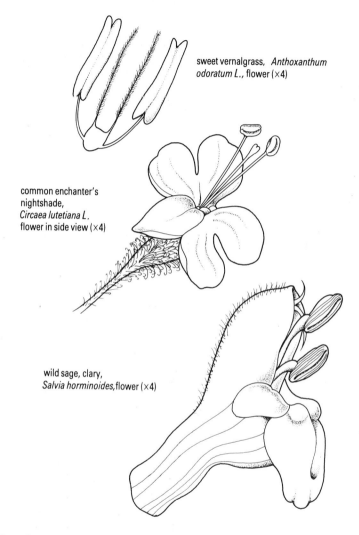

sweet vernalgrass, *Anthoxanthum odoratum L.*, flower (×4)

common enchanter's nightshade, *Circaea lutetiana L.* flower in side view (×4)

wild sage, clary, *Salvia horminoides,* flower (×4)

Figure 5
Drawings of three different genera placed by Linnaeus in the class Diandra (two stamens). They are now placed in quite separate families on the basis of other differences in the arrangement of the flower parts.

Figure 4
The 24 flowering plant families of Linnaeus. This is one of Ehret's original drawings illustrating Linnaeus' 'Sexual System' (1736) based largely on the number of stamens.

11

order was strong evidence in support of evolution. He wrote in the *Origin of species*:

> I believe that something more is included [in our classification ... than mere resemblance] and that propinquity of descent – the only known cause of similarity between organisms – is the bond, hidden as it is by various degrees of modification, which is partly revealed to us by our classification.

So it was that Darwin's work provided the theoretical background for the natural classifications which were already being produced.

The publication of Darwin's theory of evolution by natural selection did not bring about any immediate change in classifications, but one thing which did alter was the notion of a species as a fixed type. This was replaced with the idea of a species as a breeding population, the unit on which natural selection acts.

It was the rise of genetics and the study of chromosomes, DNA and protein structure which provided much new and more fundamental information on which to base new classifications, and to reassess and perhaps change existing ones. Also the development of numerical techniques and the use of computers vastly increased the capacity of taxonomists to integrate all this new information into classifications. For these reasons, what has been called a 'taxonomic explosion' has taken place in recent years.

The aim of present day taxonomists is to provide the most natural classification possible. At least three different approaches are used.

Firstly, some taxonomists classify organisms solely on the basis of their characters, without attempting to reconstruct the evolutionary relationships of the groups. This is the *phenetic* approach (see pages 14 to 21).

Secondly, there is the *phylogenetic* approach, which is based on evolutionary relationships. Haeckel's phylogeny of living things is an early example (see figure 6). In groups where the fossil history is rich, as it is for the horse, a phylogenetic classification can incorporate direct evidence of history, but this has to be treated like data from present day animals. In some groups, bacteria and fungi for instance, there is little fossil evidence available, so a classification based on present day characters is the only one possible. Phylogenetic classifications of these groups depend on inferring possible evolutionary relationships by comparing present day characters and there are many techniques for doing this. One method is shown in figure 7.

Darwin emphasized that there are two aspects to phylogeny: the

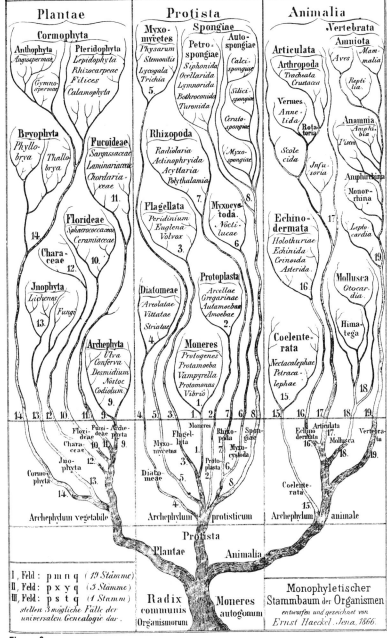

Figure 6

An early example of phylogenetic classification by Haeckel (1834–1919).

	Population							
	A	B	C	D	E	F	G	H
Character 1	+	+	−	−	−	−	−	−
2	−	−	+	+	−	−	−	−
3	−	−	+	+	+	−	−	−
4	−	−	−	−	−	+	+	+
5	+	+	+	+	+	−	−	−
6	+	+	+	+	+	+	+	+

+ character present
− character absent

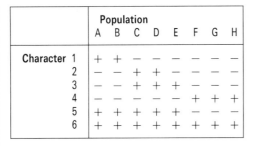

'Box-in-box' arrangement on the basis of the characters in the table

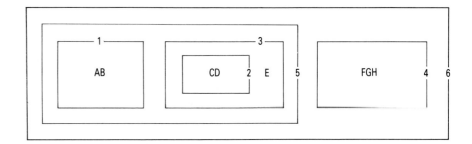

present day populations

A simple possible phylogeny

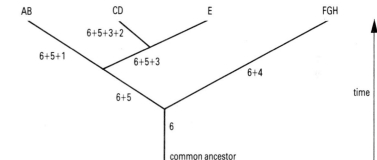

time

common ancestor

Figure 7
How a phylogeny might be inferred from present day characters.

sequence of branching of new groups from a common ancestor – the genealogy – and the degree to which the groups have continued to change ever since. Present day diversity of living things is considered by most biologists to be the result of these two processes, and evolutionary classifications are based on a combination of both.

Thirdly, there is the *cladistic* approach where it is closer common ancestry, the genealogy, which is considered to be important and not the degree to which groups have subsequently diverged.

Cladists argue that the branching of the groups from a common ancestor to form distinct species is the decisive process in evolution and that therefore a cladistic classification is the most precise and natural one. It does most closely reflect the genealogy of a group, but there are drawbacks.

For instance, because *all* the descendants of a most recent common ancestor have to be put together in a group and all the branch points indicated, the written classification becomes rather cumbersome. Reptiles, birds and mammals, which have been recognized as natural groups for a long time, illustrate the problem.

From a study of the fossil evidence it has been inferred that the birds arose from one line of reptiles and the mammals from another (see figure 8). In a cladistic classification therefore, birds and mammals would be ranked as sub-groups of the amniotes (which have an amnion, around the developing embryo). Birds and mammals, however, have changed a great deal since branching off from their respective reptilian ancestors, and the gap in resemblance between birds and reptiles and mammals and reptiles is much greater than that between the most diverse modern reptiles.

An evolutionary classification tries to combine the two facets of evolution. It tries to take account of the branching of the family tree and the degree of divergence of the groups. The result is that evolutionary classification gives reptiles, birds and mammals equal status, so although the direct information about ancestry is lost, some estimate of the degree to which birds and mammals have evolved since branching is made.

In a cladistic classification the inferred branches are reflected in the classification; where there are more than two links to the branch they

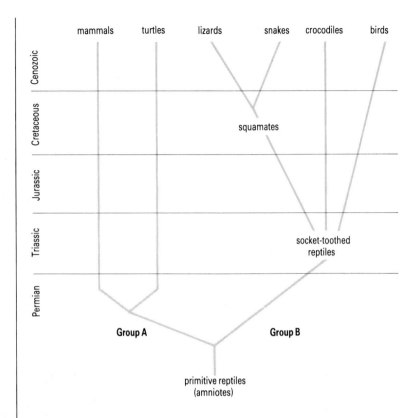

Figure 8
The evolution of reptiles, birds and mammals.

are simply listed. So from figure 8 a cladistic classification would be:

Rank 1   Amniotes
  Rank 1.1   Group A
    Rank 1.1.1   Mammals
    Rank 1.1.2   Turtles
  Rank 1.2   Group B
    Rank 1.2.1   Squamates
      Rank 1.2.1.1   Lizards
      Rank 1.2.1.2   Snakes
    Rank 1.2.2   Crocodiles
    Rank 1.2.3   Birds

In a cladistic classification the term 'reptile' does not exist. In a traditional classification the group of reptiles is deemed by consensus to contain turtles (even though they are genealogically closer to mammals), lizards, snakes and crocodiles. But this group 'reptile' is recognized on what the creatures have (an amnion) and also what they do not have (feathers or hair). This is a convention which has to be learnt. In contrast all the taxa along the top of figure 8 are recognizable groups each with their own attributes (birds with feathers, mammals with hair).

Convergence

It may be the case that present day similarities do not reflect recent common ancestry but suggest groupings the constituent members of which are not genealogically related. This is because similar features have developed separately in unrelated groups during the course of evolution – this is called convergence. Similarities between cacti and succulents, and similarities between wind-pollinated plants of many families, are illustrations of convergence (see figure 9).

Numerical taxonomists (see below) would assume that convergence need not mislead in the construction of a classification, because if enough characters are compared, the convergent characters will only form a small percentage of the overall evidence. Evolutionary and cladistic classifications both acknowledge the phenomenon of convergence, but it is difficult to decide whether an individual feature is convergent. This must always be a source of error in classification.

Although almost all taxonomists would agree that evolution has been the cause of the diversity seen in nature and most would agree that a classification which reflects this is desirable, the problems of producing one based on the evidence available are considerable. Many types of taxonomic evidence and treatments have been used in approaching this problem. These are considered in the following sections.

Numerical taxonomy

In 1763 a French taxonomist, M. Adanson, published a classification of plants called *Familles des plantes*. He had been working in Senegal and had found many new forms which he could not fit into the classifications then used, so he constructed his own. His aim was to look at overall likenesses between groups and so to produce a more natural classification. He compared as many characters as possible

a

Figure 9
A cactus and succulent illustrating convergence.
a Organ-pipe cactus in Arizona.
b Candelabra spurge (*Euphorbia* sp.) in the Canary Islands.

b

and he gave equal importance to every character used. His ideas, however, were impractical without the use of computers. Imagine comparing even ten species using 30 characters each and looking at all the correlations between them!

Modern numerical taxonomy is based on a number of principles which were laid down by R.R. Sokal and P.H.A. Sneath in their *Numerical taxonomy* which they published in 1963.

These principles which underlie the methods of numerical taxonomy as explained by Sokal and Sneath are as follows:

1 The more characters used the better the classification will be.
2 All the characters used are equally weighted (see page 16).
3 An overall similarity between two groups being compared is a function of the individual similarities in each of the many characters being compared.

4 Because correlations between the characters of the groups vary, it is possible to recognize distinct taxonomic groups.
5 Classifications produced in this way may be tested by observation and experiment.
6 Classifications are based on observable characters only (*i.e.* phenetic similarity).

In a more recent book, *Numerical taxonomy* (1973), Sneath and Sokal added another principle which was:

7 Phylogenetic inferences (*i.e.* assumptions about evolutionary pathways) may be made on the basis of the classifications.

Many of these principles resemble those put forward by Adanson and are now the ones applied to all groups of living organisms when using numerical methods of taxonomy.

OTUs		Epidermal long-cells wavy	Inflorescence spiciform	Glumes subulate	Lower glume minute	Lower glume twisted	Lemma long-awned	Lemma bifid	Lemma keeled	Lemma tuberculate	Lemma 3-veined	Lemma broadly hyaline	Hilum punctiform
Castellia	A	−	±	−	−	−	−	−	−	+	−	−	−
Catapodium	B	−	±	−	−	−	−	−	±	−	−	±	+
Ctenopsis	C	+	+	−	+	−	−	−	+	−	−	−	−
Cutandia	D	−	−	−	−	−	±	+	−	−	+	±	−
Desmazeria	E	−	±	−	−	−	−	+	−	−	±	±	+
Loliolum	F	−	+	+	−	+	−	−	−	−	−	−	−
Micropyrum	G	+	+	−	−	−	±	±	−	−	−	−	−
Narduretia	H	+	−	−	+	−	+	−	−	−	−	−	−
Narduroides	I	+	+	−	−	−	−	+	−	−	−	+	+
Vulpia	J	+	−	−	±	−	+	−	−	−	−	−	−
Vulpiella	K	−	−	−	−	−	±	+	+	−	+	−	−
Wangenheimia	L	+	+	+	−	+	−	−	+	−	−	−	−

+ presence of a character
− absence of a character
± presence or absence of a character

Table 2
A small data matrix with 12 OTUs and 12 characters. The OTUs are genera of annual grasses.

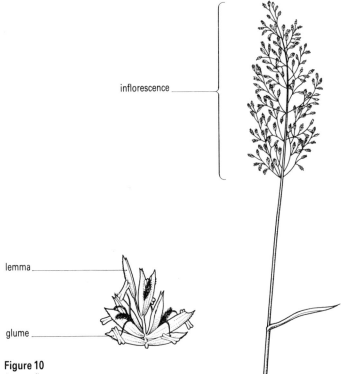

inflorescence

lemma

glume

Figure 10
A grass flower.

A simplified version of the procedure used in numerical taxonomy is given below.

1 The organisms for study are selected. The lowest ranking group in the study (which may be an individual, a family, etc.) is called the Operational Taxonomic Unit (OTU).
2 The characters for comparison are selected. At least 60, and usually 80 to 100 are used. All types of characters may be included: physiological, biochemical, morphological, etc.

The characters chosen have to be as simple as possible and must be precise. 'Leaf shape' for instance, is a combination of many variables and can be broken down into quantitative measurements like width and length, or features like the presence or absence of lobes, leaflets, etc.

Characters may also be two-state (for example, hairy or non-hairy skins) or they may be multi-state (for example, colour of petal). The characters are scored and the results plotted on a data matrix, as shown in table 2 for 12 characters of 12 genera of annual grasses. The drawing of a grass flower in figure 10 will help you to understand the characters used.
3 The similarities between OTUs are then calculated by comparing every OTU with every other, for each character. This is where the computer is used.
4 A percentage similarity is calculated between each pair of OTUs, and a similarity matrix is constructed.

The similarity matrix in figure 11a is a simple illustration. It is shaded to show up the closely related OTUs. Figure 11b is the same matrix rearranged by visually clustering together OTUs which are similar to each other. This 'clustering' is usually done mathematically since, with a large number of OTUs and characters, visual sorting becomes very difficult.

Once the degree of clustering of the OTUs has been worked out the results may be shown as a phenogram (figure 12).

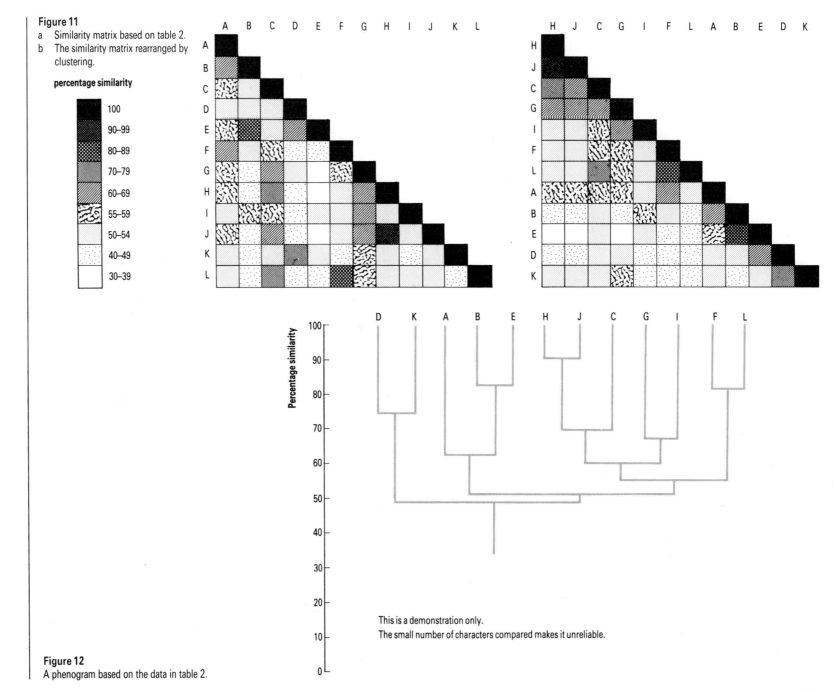

Figure 11
a Similarity matrix based on table 2.
b The similarity matrix rearranged by clustering.

percentage similarity

Figure 12
A phenogram based on the data in table 2.

This is a demonstration only.
The small number of characters compared makes it unreliable.

STUDY ITEM 1
Classifying by a numerical method

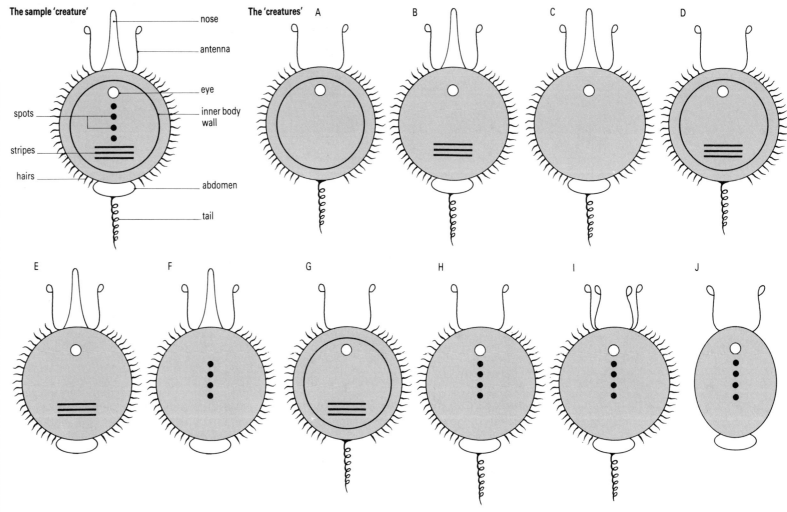

The sample 'creature' — nose, antenna, eye, inner body wall, spots, stripes, hairs, abdomen, tail

The 'creatures' A, B, C, D, E, F, G, H, I, J

Figure 13
a   A sample 'creature' with parts labelled.
b   'Creatures' A – J.

The working out of this item is an optional exercise. Questions c to e at the end of this study item may be answered by studying figure 13 (the drawings of the 'creatures') and figure 14 (the phenogram).

The ten 'creatures' A to J in figure 13b exhibit various combinations of characters as shown in the sample 'creature' (figure 13a).

Character / Creature	1 Body circular	2	3	4	5	6	7	8	9	10
A	+									
B	+									
C	+									
D	+									
E	+									
F	+									
G	+									
H	+									
I	+									
J	−									

Table 3
A data matrix used to make comparisons between pairs of 'creatures' easier.

Creature	A	B	C	D	E	F	G	H	I	J
A	100									
B		100								
C		90	100							
D		70		100						
E		90			100					
F		60				100				
G		70					100			
H		70						100		
I		60							100	
J		40								100

Percentage similarity

Table 4
This is a similarity matrix

a Looking at A to J, find ten characters that can be scored in two states on a table such as the one above.

b When the data matrix is complete, draw a table like table 4 and compare each pair of 'creatures' (A with B, A with C, A with D and so on), counting up the number of characters in which they match. Both positive and negative matches count. Before putting the score into the table, it needs conversion to a percentage (in this case you multiply by 10).

By shading table 4 as has been done in figure 11a groups of similar 'creatures' should appear. If you redraw the matrix grouping similar 'creatures' together, for example B next to E, then the clusters of similar 'creatures' become more obvious, and this is all the treatment which is needed to sort the 'creatures' into groups. (This type of regrouping is shown in figure 11b.)

Normally a numerical taxonomist will be dealing with many more than ten OTUs and many more characters, so a computer is used to work out similarity coefficients and to cluster similar OTUs together. The results can then be displayed in a phenogram.

Figure 14 on the next page is one possible phenogram showing the groupings of the 'creatures' A to J.

c Which 'creature' is least like any other?

A phenogram may be regarded as representing a conventional taxonomic hierarchy. For example, it may be decided that, in this case, creatures more than 85 per cent similar to each other would be placed in the same genus, those more than 65 per cent similar in the same family and those more than 55 per cent similar in the same order, with all the creatures A to J being placed in the same class.

d If you do this, how many genera and how many orders have you produced?

e Construct a box-in-box classification (see page 7) to illustrate this hierarchy. (Assume that each 'creature' represents a different species except D and G which are identical.)

Numerical taxonomists often do not use the conventional ranks such as genus or family but simply refer directly to the degree of

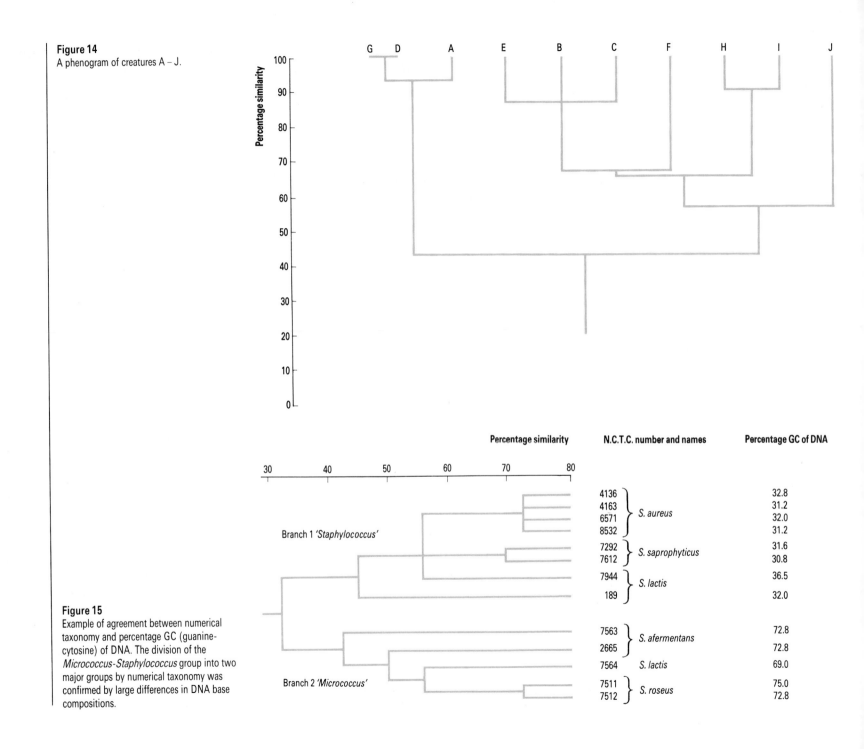

Figure 14
A phenogram of creatures A – J.

Figure 15
Example of agreement between numerical taxonomy and percentage GC (guanine-cytosine) of DNA. The division of the *Micrococcus-Staphylococcus* group into two major groups by numerical taxonomy was confirmed by large differences in DNA base compositions.

similarity between a group. The groups A, D, G, or B, E, C, or H, I, would be 85-phenons (groups defined by an 85 per cent similarity).

The applications of numerical taxonomy

The techniques of numerical taxonomy have been applied particularly to groups such as the bacteria where previous classification, especially at the species level, was sometimes uncertain.

Figure 15 shows an example where numerical treatment and a DNA analysis have been used together to sort out the *Staphylococcus* group. The agreement between the two types of data makes the classification much more satisfactory.

In the field of medicine the technique has been applied to cases of acute leukaemia (figure 16).

Using numerical taxonomic methods four groups of acute leukaemia were found. One group, P, has distinct clinical features; there is some overlap between R and Q; and there is considerable overlap between R and S. Nearly all cases of acute leukaemia fit into these groups, whereas previously the classification had been uncertain.

There are other clinical problems to which these techniques could obviously be applied. Their success will depend on choosing the best applications and using reliable procedures. If a computer can produce reliable results, this will leave the physicians more time to tackle the problems they alone can solve.

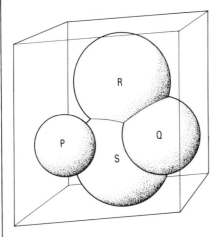

P - erythraemic myelosis
Q - lymphoblastic
R - myelomonocytic
S - myeloblastic

Figure 16
Classification of acute leukaemia cases. The four groups are shown in one view of a model of the relationships. Each sphere represents a cluster of individual cases.

Current methods used in taxonomy

We have already seen that many types of characters are useful in classifying, and many sources of information contribute to improving classifications. The aim of much current work is to improve the understanding of the phylogeny of the organisms studied by using recently developed techniques.

Today a taxonomic study of any group of organisms will combine the work of many specialists. It might involve some, or all, of the steps in the flowchart (figure 17).

Examples of some of the techniques used in the various areas of study in the flowchart are described in this section.

Structural characters

The major part of the evidence on which we classify living organisms has always been structural. The morphology and anatomy of higher plants and animals, including that of embryos and various developmental stages as well as of mature adults, provide characters which are easy to observe and therefore widely useful. Many taxonomists spend their time identifying and classifying previously unknown specimens. There are obvious advantages in being able to do this by observing external features rather than, say, by analysing the petal pigments of a flower.

The development of microscopy has extended the range of structural characters which can be classified. The scanning electron microscope, which combines high magnification, good resolution and great depth of focus, has been used for example in studies of pollen grains, fruit and seed surfaces and leaf surfaces.

Figure 18 shows seeds from the different sub-species of *Montia fontana* (water blinks). These sub-species are separable only on the basis of their seed morphology, and the scanning electron micrographs clearly illustrate the differences. This method is particularly useful in the study of fossil plants when pollen grains or seeds are the only parts remaining.

Transmission electron microscopy, which enables very high magnification, high resolution studies of internal structure, has been of great importance in contributing evidence which led to the basic division of living cells into prokaryotic (organisms without an organized nucleus) cells and eukaryotic (true nucleus) cells (see pages 32 and 33). The differences which exist between prokaryotes and eukaryotes led to biologists acknowledging a fundamental distinction

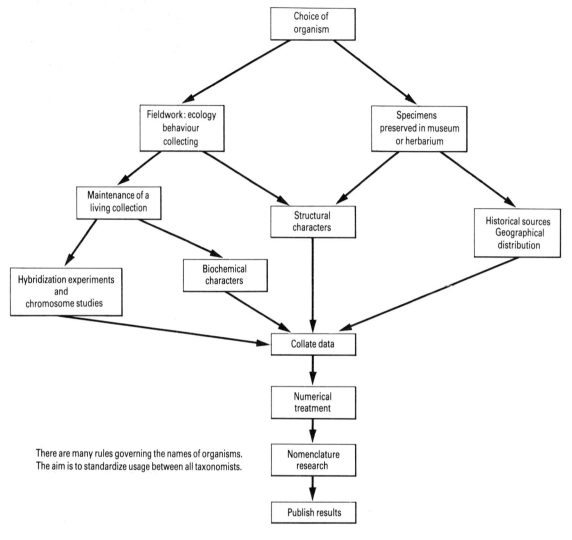

Figure 17
A taxonomic flowchart showing areas of study.

Choice of organism

Fieldwork: ecology behaviour collecting

Specimens preserved in museum or herbarium

Maintenance of a living collection

Structural characters

Historical sources Geographical distribution

Hybridization experiments and chromosome studies

Biochemical characters

Collate data

Numerical treatment

Nomenclature research

There are many rules governing the names of organisms. The aim is to standardize usage between all taxonomists.

Publish results

between these two types of cell. Indeed, the differences are much more significant than those previously recognized between plant and animal cells which had led to the establishment of the separate disciplines of botany and zoology.

Biochemical characters

In organisms which have few easily observed structural characters, such as the bacteria, biochemical characters have long been used in classification. More recently there has been an enormous expansion in the study and use of biochemical characters in all groups. This is because new techniques have been developed and it has become possible to study potentially important characters such as the structure of DNA and proteins.

The biochemical techniques used include chromatography, electrophoresis, DNA hybridization and sequence analysis of proteins.

Figure 18
Scanning electronmicrograph of seeds of the
four sub-species of *Montia fontana.*
a   Subsp. *fontana.*
b   Subsp. *variabilis.*
c   Subsp. *amporitana.*
d   Subsp. *chondrosperma.*

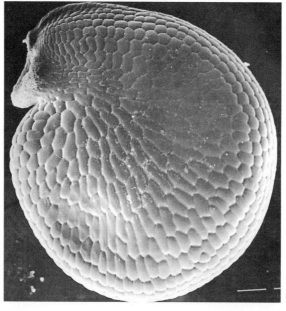

a

b

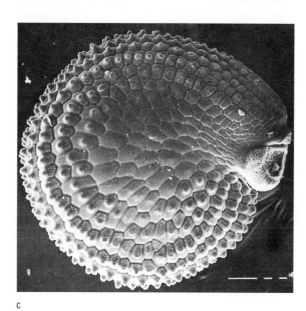

c

d

STUDY ITEM 2
An application of chromatography in taxonomy

The 'tea problem' is a good example of a biochemical technique (paper chromatography) being used to resolve a taxonomic problem where morphological differences are not clear cut.

There are two main types of tea, *Camellia sinensis* subspecies *sinensis* (China tea) and *Camellia sinensis* subspecies *assamica* (Assam tea). These differ from each other in leaf and shoot morphology: China tea having dull, small leaves with anthocyanin pigments in the shoot and Assam tea having large, glossy, green leaves without anthocyanin pigments. (These pigments are a common source of red or blue colours in many plants.)

Tea plantations consist of the two types and the many hybrids which exist between them. Local names are used for the different tea varieties, but it is impossible to sort out the pedigree of any particular tea on the basis of morphology alone.

Paper chromatography has proved to be particularly useful because it can be applied to processed tea leaves, and therefore any tea offered for sale can be investigated. The phenolic compounds of which several are present in tea are examined here. Some of these are the 'tannins' which gave tea its astringent flavour and black colour when fermented. Anthocyanins, although phenolic, are not included in table 5.

a Which compound suggests 'China' ancestry?
b Suggest a possible ancestry for tea type *e*.

Type *f*, the Southern form, has large glossy leaves and anthocyanin present. It has been suggested that it should be a third sub-species of *Camellia sinensis*.

c Suggest how tea type *f* could have arisen.
d Suggest a possible ancestry for tea type *h*.

STUDY ITEM 3
Electrophoresis in taxonomy

Electrophoresis is based on the principle that in a mixture of proteins, each protein will, because of its own characteristic electric charge, respond to an applied electrical potential in a characteristic way, different at different pH values. The proteins can therefore be separated (figure 19).

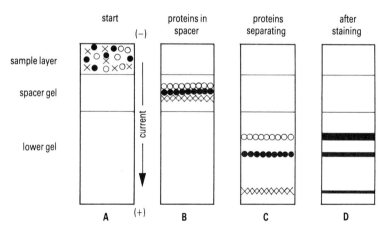

Figure 19
The separation of a protein mixture into narrow bands within gel columns by discontinuous electrophoresis. The test sample is placed on top of the column containing two gels differing in pore diameter (A). The upper gel has a large pore size and allows the initial sorting of proteins into a closely layered stack of discs (B). The lower gel allows these protein fractions to separate out into bands (C). These separated protein bands can be seen by applying specific stains (D).

This process has been used for example to compare enzyme distribution in species of *Corynebacterium* (table 6).

Tea variety	Phenolic compounds present		
	A	B	C
a Assam	+ +	?	?
b China	+	0	+ + +
c Experimental *a,b* cross	+	0	+ + +
d Ceylon (1)	+	0	+ + +
e Ceylon (2)	+ +	0	+
f Southern form	+ + +	+ + +	0
g Suspected *f,a* cross	+ + +	+ +	0
h 'Intermediate' type	+ + +	+ +	+
i *Camellia taliensis* (non-tea *Camellia*)	+ + +	+ + +	0

? Barely detectable   + +   Increasing concentration
+
+ + +

Table 5
Results of chromatography.

Corynebacterium		Enzyme distribution		
Species	**Ecology**	Number of esterases	Number of catalases	Number of peroxidases
diptheriae 1	human pathogens	–	1	–
diptheriae 2		–	1	–
diptheriae 3		–	1	–
ulcerans		–	1	–
xerosis		–	1	–
hofmanni		–	1	–
haemolyticum		3	1	–
renale	animal pathogens	–	2	–
bovis		–	2	–
ovis		–	2	–
equi		–	2	–
pyogenes 1		3	–	–
pyogenes 2		3	–	–
fascians 1	plant pathogens	2	2	1
fascians 2		3	2	1
tritici		2	1	1
betae		4	1	1
poinsettiae		1	1	1
flaccumfaciens		1	1	1
manihot	saprophytes	2	1	1
aquaticum		4	1	1
mediolanum		2	1	–
acetoacidophilum		1	1	–
rubrum		4	2	–

Table 6
Enzyme distribution in species of *Corynebacterium*.

a Could you use this method to determine whether an unknown species of *Corynebacterium* was a human pathogen?

b Can species of *Corynebacterium* which are plant pathogens be distinguished from those species which are saprophytes by this method?

Electrophoresis has also been used in the case of crops where a clear knowledge of the genetic variability of a plant can help in the development of breeding programmes in which experimental crosses with near relations could improve production. For example, a variation available in wild wheat might be needed in future breeding programmes to introduce a new character into cultivated wheats, which have become very specialized. The proteins of wild wheat can be investigated by electrophoresis to detect what genetic variation is available.

DNA studies

The role of DNA as the complete blueprint for the construction and maintenance of an organism means that DNA structure has become an important taxonomic character. Since mutations are changes in DNA, the differences in DNA structure may be regarded as a record of the steps by which related groups have diverged during evolution. Direct comparison of DNA base sequences is technically difficult, but other means of comparing DNA from different species can be used.

One method is DNA hybridization. The two complementary strands of the DNA double helix are dissociated from each other by heating to 100°C and cooling rapidly. If single strands from two species are mixed together under suitable conditions hybrid DNA helices may be formed if there is some similarity between the two DNA samples (figure 20).

Furthermore, if one of the samples is radioactively labelled, the amount of hybrid DNA produced can be assessed.

Hybrid DNA is less stable on heating than reassociated helices of the same species. This is because the base sequences are not completely matched. The temperature at which the reassociated strands are 50 per cent dissociated (T_m) is used to compare hybrid DNA with 'parental' DNA. A T_m difference of 1°C is equivalent to about 1.5 per cent difference in bases between the two DNAs.

This process has been useful in bacterial classification (see figure 15). It has also been used in other groups to attempt to assess evolutionary relationships and to check traditional classifications.

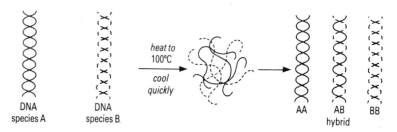

Figure 20
DNA hybridization.

STUDY ITEM 4
DNA hybridization of some cereal crops

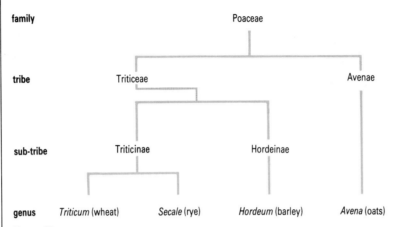

Figure 21
A traditional classification of some cereal crops.

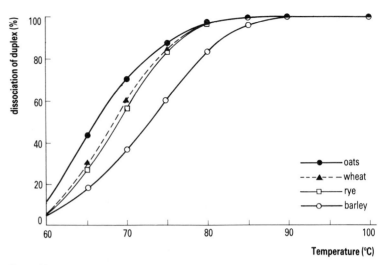

Figure 22
Thermal stability profiles of DNA/DNA hybrids of barley–oats, barley–wheat, barley–rye and barley–barley. Barley DNA was immobilized on filters in each case.

Figure 21 shows the traditional classification of some of the cereal crops. DNA hybridization carried out under carefully controlled conditions has been used to check this classification.

In these experiments one of the DNAs was present as long single strands fixed on a filter. The other DNA, radioactively labelled, broken into short segments and dissociated into single strands, was reacted with it.

Filter bound DNA	Radioactively labelled DNA % binding			
	Barley	Oats	Rye	Wheat
Barley	100	19	58	72
Oats	12	100	15	17
Rye	59	22	100	–
Wheat	48	16	60	100

Table 7
Relative percentage of binding of DNA hybrid helices from cereals.

a Do these results support the placing of oats in a separate tribe from other cereals in the traditional classification?

b Do these results support the placing of wheat and rye in a different sub-tribe from barley in the traditional classification?

c What are the T_m values for each of the DNA hybrids shown on the graph in figure 22?

d If a 1 °C reduction in T_m represents a 1.5% difference in bases, what would be the percentage base differences of the other cereals from barley?

Sequence analysis of proteins

There are a number of reasons why this technique has become of major importance in systematics.

Firstly, since proteins are coded for in DNA they represent a copy of the sequence of genetic information, DNA base sequences having been translated into amino acid sequences. Analysis of amino acid sequences in proteins can give a new means of comparing organisms which reflects the genotypes of the organisms to a greater extent than other characters.

Secondly, proteins are widely distributed throughout nature and so they can be used for comparisons at many levels, and for comparing very unlike organisms.

Thirdly, methods for determining the sequences of amino acids are well developed.

The best known protein in this context is cytochrome *c*.

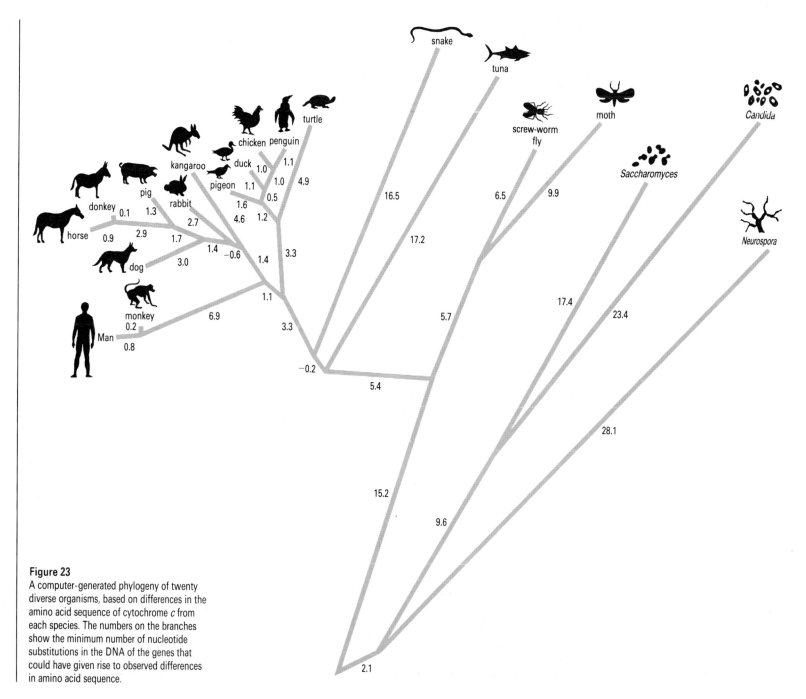

Figure 23
A computer-generated phylogeny of twenty diverse organisms, based on differences in the amino acid sequence of cytochrome *c* from each species. The numbers on the branches show the minimum number of nucleotide substitutions in the DNA of the genes that could have given rise to observed differences in amino acid sequence.

Cytochrome *c* is a protein of just over 100 amino acids which is substantially similar over a wide range of animals, plants, bacteria and fungi. The sequences of amino acids for many cytochromes c have been established. Once this is done the procedure is as follows:

1 The cytochrome c amino acid sequences to be compared are lined up so that homologous amino acid positions can be compared.
2 The amino acids of the cytochromes are then compared pair by pair. Wherever an amino acid difference exists between the two cytochromes, the minimum number of mutations which would be needed to change the genetic code from one amino acid to another is calculated.
3 The minimum number of mutations which would be needed to change one cytochrome c to another is calculated.

STUDY ITEM 5
Evidence from cytochrome *c*

Figure 23 is an example of a wide ranging comparison of cytochrome *c*, where a computer has been used to compare the cytochrome and to generate a phylogeny based on their differences. The numbers on the branches indicate the minimum number of nucleotide base changes that could have given rise to the differences observed.

Considering that this is based on the structure of one protein molecule only, the relationships seem to fit in well with traditional classifications and with what is known from fossils.

a Can you see any relationships which do not agree with traditional classifications?

The relevance of systematics in contemporary biology

Paradoxically, systematics is of such essential importance in biology that its role may be easily overlooked. A researcher working with the bacterium *Bacillus subtilis* may not be concerned with the characteristics which identify this species, but he needs to be confident that other people will understand what he means by *Bacillus subtilis* and that other researchers working with it are using the same species. A naturalist finding a strange insect will also be confident that a place can be found in an insect classification for the creature. He might not be able to identify it himself, perhaps nobody will have seen its like before; but it will be named, described and fitted into an appropriate slot in the classification.

Systematics allows us to describe the diversity of living things and to attempt to understand and to make the best possible use of this diversity. The examples included in this section illustrate these aspects of systematics.

Improving wheat productivity

Although wheat production has increased dramatically in the last 20 years, it will have to expand still further to meet the needs of a hungry world. Fertilizers and pesticides are prohibitively expensive and increased production will depend on the production of new varieties, either with increased yield or with new ecological adaptations which would allow them to be grown in climates where wheat cannot be grown today.

However, there are problems that hinder such development. Intensive breeding programmes have produced modern wheat varieties which are very invariable, consisting of a single genotype only. Also the genetic material of the cultivated wheats has already been widely used in breeding experiments, so the chances of producing any more new varieties in this way are small.

Figure 24 shows the species of wheat cultivated today. Many of the older cultivated varieties have already been lost, with a loss of reserves of genetic variability which might have been used in breeding programmes. Attempts to produce new varieties by chemical or radiation treatment have been largely unproductive.

One promising area of research, however, is to undertake breeding experiments with the near relatives of cultivated wheat which are still to be found in the wild (figure 25).

The Triticeae tribe of grasses consists of 14 genera grouped into two sub-tribes, Triticinae and Hordeinae (see also DNA hybridization, page 25). Within both sub-tribes occasional hybridization is possible, and successful crosses have also been produced between members of the two sub-tribes.

There are a number of wild diploid wheats which have distinct genotypes and differ in morphology, ecology and geographical distribution. They are mostly found in south–west Asia and are adapted to conditions ranging from cool, humid mountains to hot, dry plains. Amongst the desirable characters found in these wild wheats are improved quality and quantity of grain protein; tolerance

Figure 24
Cultivated species of *Triticum* (wheat).

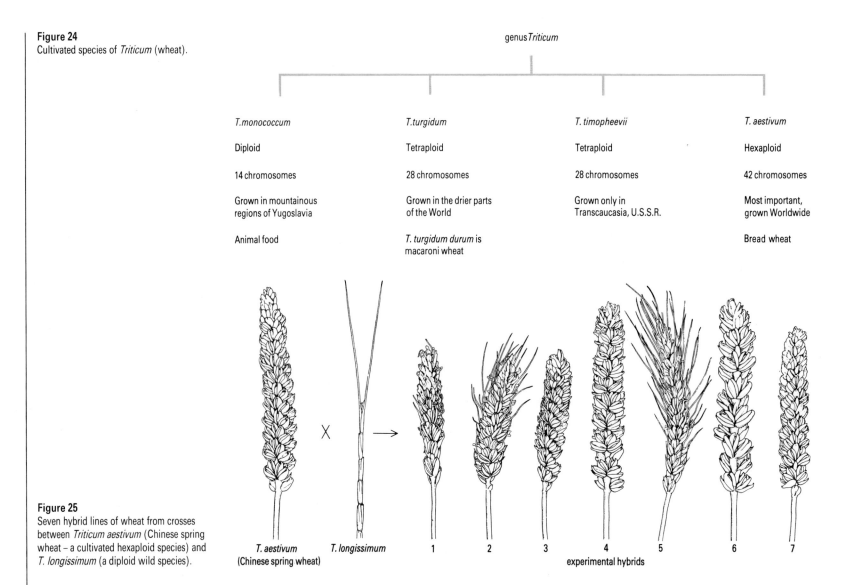

genus *Triticum*

T.monococcum	*T.turgidum*	*T. timopheevii*	*T. aestivum*
Diploid	Tetraploid	Tetraploid	Hexaploid
14 chromosomes	28 chromosomes	28 chromosomes	42 chromosomes
Grown in mountainous regions of Yugoslavia	Grown in the drier parts of the World	Grown only in Transcaucasia, U.S.S.R.	Most important, grown Worldwide
Animal food	*T. turgidum durum* is macaroni wheat		Bread wheat

T. aestivum (Chinese spring wheat)   *T. longissimum*   1   2   3   4   5   6   7
experimental hybrids

Figure 25
Seven hybrid lines of wheat from crosses between *Triticum aestivum* (Chinese spring wheat – a cultivated hexaploid species) and *T. longissimum* (a diploid wild species).

of heat and of salty soils; winter hardiness; resistance to fungal and viral diseases, insects, drought and lodging (flattening in rain and wind); and earlier ripening time. Adding these desirable characters to cultivated wheat is not straightforward, for many reasons.

There have been some successes: for example, the gene for stripe-rust resistance has been successfully transferred from the wild diploid *T. comosum* to *T. aestivum*. Addition of a whole set of chromosomes has also led to successful hybrid forms. A cross between a tetraploid wheat, *T. turgidum,* and diploid *Secale cereale* (rye) which is another genus in the sub-tribe Triticinae, has given rise to a new hexaploid crop, *Triticale,* which combines the winter hardiness and rust resistance of rye with the high yield of wheat. In trials this crop out-yielded wheat in some areas. In Mexico the highest *Triticale* yield was 8350 kg per hectare compared with 7245 kg per hectare for wheat.

Figure 26
The two species which are the principal
carriers of the Dutch elm disease fungus:
Scolytus multistriatus, the European species,
and *Hylurgopinus rufipes*, the North American
species.

 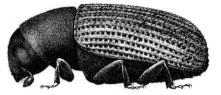

Scolytus multistriatus   *Hylurgopinus rufipes*

Triticale has a high content of essential amino acids and is suitable for all traditional cereal uses. First generation hybrid plants (which are sterile tripoids) have to be treated with a chemical which causes chromosome doubling in order to produce fertile hexaploid *Triticale*.

Future exploitation of wheat relatives for the improvement of cultivated wheat depends on improved systematic knowledge of the wild species and on collecting and maintaining samples of all the species as a reserve of genes.

The problem of Dutch elm disease

This disease, first observed in 1919, has killed millions of trees in Europe and America, and has changed the face of the southern English countryside. Many European and American elm species are susceptible: *Ulmus americana, U. rubra, U. thomasii, U. serotina, U. alata, U. laevis,* and *U. procera.* Asian species, *U. parvifolia* and *U. pumila,* are resistant. The fungus which causes the disease is *Ceratocystis ulmi.* Many species of insects carry the spores of the fungus, but only elm bark beetles *Scolytus multistriatus* and *Scolytus scolytus* (in Europe) and *Hylurgopinus rufipes* (in America) are found to transmit the infection (figure 26).

Once the species involved were identified correctly, control methods could be attempted. Preventive treatment by use of insecticides and fungicides proved very costly. Fungicides have also proved relatively ineffective against *Ceratocystis ulmi.* Pheromones, chemicals which attract elm bark beetles, have been used successfully in trapping beetles and so cutting down the infection rate of trees. Another approach which has recently been successful is the production of an antifungal agent. A range of species of the bacterium genus *Pseudomonas* was screened for production of a chemical which would inhibit the growth of *Ceratocystis ulmi.* *Pseudomonas syringae* was particularly effective. This has produced encouraging results in preventing the establishment of infection in elm trees.

Figure 27 summarizes the role of taxonomists in studying this problem.

Systematics is therefore far from a purely academic study. It plays a vital role in meeting urgent needs such as improving crop yields and controlling pests, both of which make a contribution towards solving the problem of food shortages in some parts of the World.

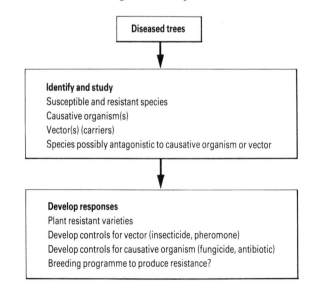

Figure 27
The role of the taxonomist in studying the problems of Dutch elm disease.

Classification

Introduction: how many kingdoms?

The natural division of macroscopic organisms into plants (green, rooted, photosynthetic organisms) and animals (mobile, food ingesting organisms) formed the basis for a two kingdom system of classification which resulted in the separate disciplines of botany and zoology being established. Mosses, algae, and fungi were attached to the plant kingdom and as they were discovered and described so were bacteria, because, like plants, they possessed a rigid cell wall.

However, there are a number of disadvantages to this traditional system. For instance, to which kingdom should unicellular organisms such as *Euglena* species (see figure 52) be assigned? These organisms and others like them can photosynthesize, swim, and move in relation to a light stimulus, thus combining typical plant and animal characteristics. As early as 1866 Haeckel suggested a third kingdom for this group of organisms. Also, can the inclusion of the fungi in the plant kingdom be justified? Fungi lack chlorophyll and therefore the ability to photosynthesize. They have an absorptive method of nutrition. They also have a very different structure from all other plants. Anomalies such as these led biologists to question a system which required all organisms to be classified as either plants or animals.

Studies of cell structure and biochemistry have shown that a major divergence between organisms does exist at the cellular level. This fundamental difference is between organisms without nuclei, called prokaryotes; and those with nuclei, called eukaryotes. The other features which distinguish these two groups are illustrated in figure 28 and table 8.

	Prokaryotes	Eukaryotes
Organisms represented	bacteria and cyanobacteria	protista, fungi, plants, and animals
Cell size	small, generally 1 μm to 5 μm	large, generally 5 μm to 100 μm
Metabolism and photosynthesis	anaerobic or aerobic; enormous variety of metabolic patterns	aerobic*; same metabolic patterns: Embden–Meyerhof pathway, Krebs cycle, oxidation, cytochrome electron transport chains
Motile structures	rigid flagella made of the protein flagellin	flexible cilia or flagella constructed of microtubules †
Cell walls	of characteristic sugars and peptides	of cellulose in plants; chitin and other glucans in fungi; lacking in animals
Organelles	no membrane bounded organelles	membrane bounded organelles, mitochondria, and chloroplasts, etc.
Genetic organization	loop of DNA in cytoplasm	DNA organized in chromosomes and bounded by nuclear membrane
Reproduction	by binary fission	by mitosis or meiosis and binary fission
Cellular organization	mainly unicellular	mainly multicellular with differentiation of cells, but some protists unicellular

* Some parasitic forms are anarobes.
† The term undulipodia has been proposed to replace eukaryote flagella and cilia.

Table 8

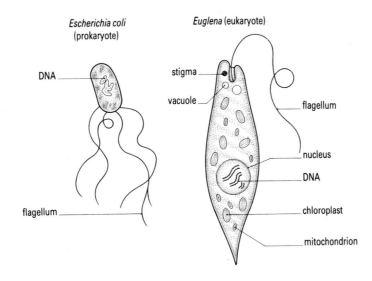

Figure 28
Drawings of a prokaryote and a eukaryote.

During the last twenty years systems having between two kingdoms (Prokaryota and Eukaryota) and eighteen have been proposed. These have attempted to take into account new evidence and ideas about the relationships of organisms. No one system may be wholly satisfactory; but any classification which gives an order to the variety of life that is more 'natural' than the traditional (plants and animals) system should also be more acceptable to biologists.

The classification in figure 29 is a five kingdom system first drawn up by Whittaker in 1969, and revised by Margulis in 1982 and Barnes in 1984.

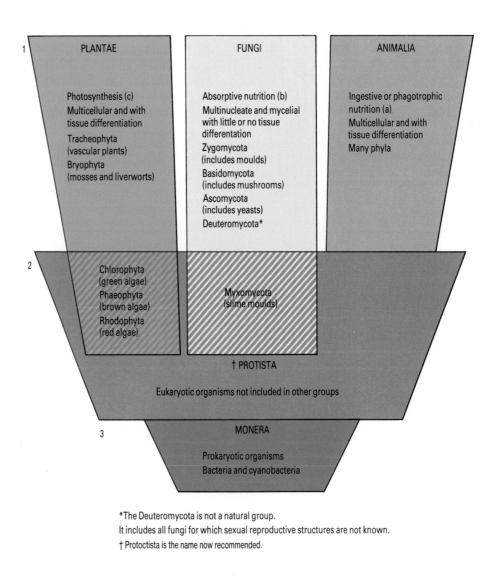

Figure 29
The five kingdom classification, mainly after Margulis, 1982, and Barnes, 1984. The hatched areas show the groups Whittaker included in Plantae and Fungi. 1, 2, and 3 refer to Whittaker's three levels, and a, b, and c to his three methods of nutrition.

*The Deuteromycota is not a natural group.
It includes all fungi for which sexual reproductive structures are not known.
† Protoctista is the name now recommended.

Whittaker based his five kingdoms on two main considerations:

1 The 'level of organization' of the organism. He recognized three levels: (1) prokaryotes, (2) unicellular eukaryotes, and (3) multicellular eukaryotes.

2 The mode of nutrition. Whittaker argued that the three major modes of nutrition, (a) ingestive (animals), (b) absorptive (fungi), and (c) photosynthetic (plants), have led to different pathways of evolution, each group becoming highly adapted to its way of life. There were drawbacks to Whittaker's classification. Some groups, Chlorophyta for example, contained unicellular and multicellular species, so these did not fit easily into the scheme. Also, some groups (such as euglenoids) exhibit more than one type of nutrition. More fundamentally, a 'natural' system of classification seeks to group closely related species together. In his scheme, Plantae in particular included groups which are thought to have evolved independently. Also the group called Protista which contained the unicellular eukaryotes represented many diverging evolutionary pathways. In the modifications by Barnes in 1984 and by Margulis in 1982 shown in figure 29, some groups of organisms (for example red and brown algae) have been removed from Plantae, making it a more natural group. This, however, makes an even wider group of Protista, as it now contains some simple multicellular organisms as well as unicellular ones.

It is generally recognized that the Protista constitutes an unsatisfactory group but it is retained because of the lack of a more satisfactory alternative. The aim of this classification is to give the features which characterize the major groups of organisms, and in most cases it does not go further than the rank of class. If it is compared with other classifications, differences will be found, mainly in the endings of the proper names of the groups described. These variations arise because taxonomists make different decisions about the relative rank of a group. For example in this classification the Scots pine, *Pinus sylvestris,* is in the class Coniferopsida (conifers) but other classifications may describe the conifers as a phylum (Coniferophyta) or an order (Coniferales). Any one classification should be internally consistent in the naming of the groups.

Viruses have been omitted because all the organisms in this classification are cellular. Viruses consist only of a strand of nucleic acid and a protein coat. They are obligate parasites. They can neither grow nor reproduce outside the cells of their host. If they were included they would form another kingdom.

KINGDOM MONERA

All Monera are prokaryotes and share all the prokaryotic features (see table 8). The group contains all bacteria including cyanobacteria (formerly called blue–green algae).

Apart from the prokaryote features which they share, bacteria are extremely diverse. Both structural and metabolic characters are needed to identify them. For example, Gram's stain is universally used to distinguish differences in bacterial cell walls. The different sorts of characters used, however, do not correlate well. If, for instance, bacteria which look alike are grouped together, each group will exhibit a whole range of different ways of living. Present classifications of bacteria are artificial. The groupings within Monera in this classification are arbitrary ones used for convenience. The analysis of nucleic acid sequences of bacteria promises to provide a classification of bacteria which will reflect their true relationships.

Using biochemical characteristics, workers in the U.S.A. have established that certain bacteria (Archaebacteria) are fundamentally different from the rest (Eubacteria). These two groups are ranked at the level of sub-kingdom (or even kingdom).

The Archaebacteria include a small number of chemo-autotrophs and methanogenic bacteria. The Eubacteria contain the majority of prokaryotes. This division is not included here as at the moment it is difficult to give the complete story and it has yet to receive widespread recognition.

Table 9 is intended to display some of the immense variety of bacterial life. It has 16 groups based on various structural and metabolic features. Only representative genera in each phylum are listed or described.

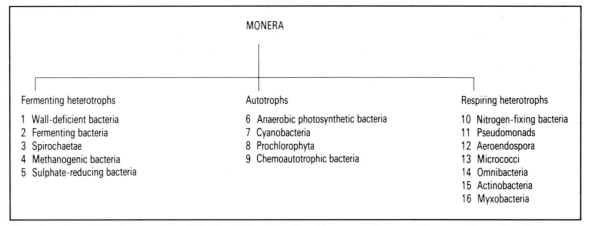

MONERA

Fermenting heterotrophs
1 Wall-deficient bacteria
2 Fermenting bacteria
3 Spirochaetae
4 Methanogenic bacteria
5 Sulphate-reducing bacteria

Autotrophs
6 Anaerobic photosynthetic bacteria
7 Cyanobacteria
8 Prochlorophyta
9 Chemoautotrophic bacteria

Respiring heterotrophs
10 Nitrogen-fixing bacteria
11 Pseudomonads
12 Aeroendospora
13 Micrococci
14 Omnibacteria
15 Actinobacteria
16 Myxobacteria

All members of group 14 and some members of 11, 12, and 13 are able to live without oxygen if necessary. One genus of group 3 requires oxygen.

Table 9
A classification of the Monera.

Fermenting heterotrophs (groups 1 to 5)

These ferment organic compounds to obtain energy.

1 Wall-deficient bacteria

These tiny organisms lack the cell walls which all other bacteria have.

An example is the genus *Mycoplasma*. Some mycoplasmas cause a type of pneumonia in humans and other animals.

Another interesting genus is *Thermoplasma* (a genus which is included in the Archaebacteria, see page 35). The single species *T. acidophilum* lives in the hot springs of Yellowstone Park at about 60°C and at a pH of 1 or 2.

2 Fermenting bacteria

The genera *Lactobacillus*, *Streptococcus*, and *Leuconostoc* are well known sugar fermenters, especially in milk, producing lactic acid amongst other compounds. They are used in the production of yoghurt, cheeses, sauerkraut, pickles, and silage.

The genus *Clostridium* includes several highly dangerous species which produce poisons. The heat resistant spores which *Clostridium botulinum* produces sometimes survive inadequate sterilization in home food bottling and canning and can cause the fatal food poisoning botulism. *Clostridium tetani* produces an almost equally potent poison causing tetanus.

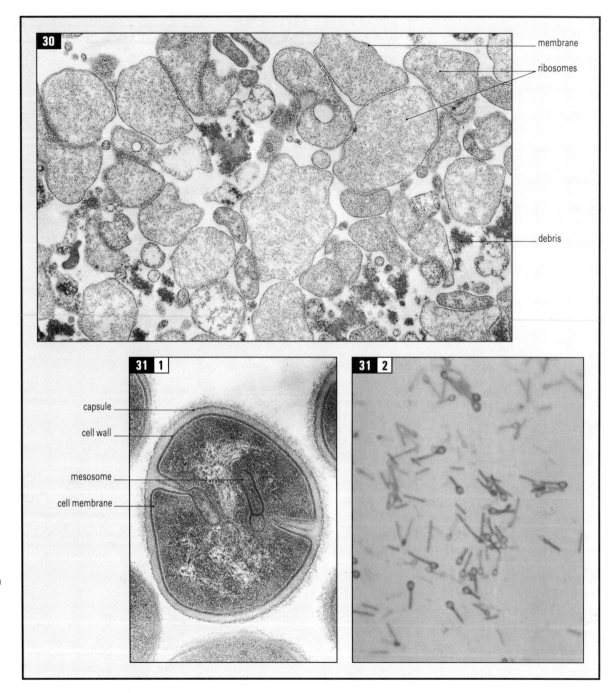

Figure 30

Electronmicrograph of a section of *Mycoplasma pulmonis* (× 120 000) which causes pneumonia in mice. Each mycoplasma contains ribosomes and is surrounded by a membrane. The black areas are debris from the broth in which the organisms were grown.

Figure 31

1 Electronmicrograph of a divid cell of *Streptococcus* (× 50 000) showing typical bacterial features.

2 *Clostridium tetani* (× 100) showing the characteristic terminal spores.

3 Spirochaetae

Spirochaetes can swim by means of a rotational movement.
The species *Treponema pallidum* is the cause of syphilis.

4 Methanogenic bacteria (also included in Archaebacteria)

These unusual bacteria produce methane from hydrogen and carbon dioxide. They are widely found in sewage, digestive systems (especially of ruminants), and mud. They have a number of features which suggest that they are not closely related to other bacteria.

5 Sulphate-reducing bacteria

These bacteria require sulphate for respiration and reduce it to sulphur or hydrogen sulphide.

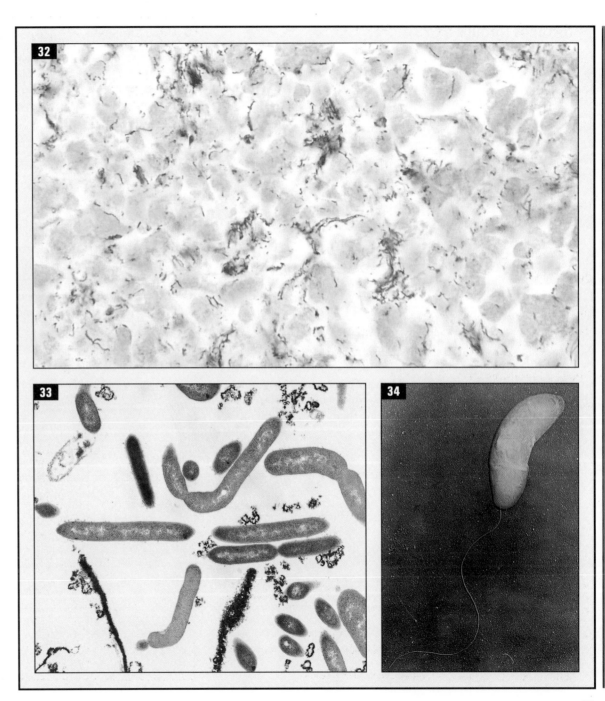

Figure 32
Light micrograph of the anaerobic spirochaete bacteria *Treponema pallidum* ($\times$ 1500) in human liver tissue.

Figure 33
Transmission electronmicrograph of *Methanobrevibacter arboriphilicus* ($\times$ 15 000). It is found in anaerobic conditions.

Figure 34
Electronmicrograph of *Desulfovibrio desulfuricans* ($\times$ 130 000), a sulphate-reducing bacterium.

Autotrophs (groups 6 to 9)

6 Anaerobic photosynthetic bacteria

These bacteria contain bacterial chlorophylls and carotenoid pigments. Unlike plants and cyanobacteria they do not use water as a source of hydrogen in photosynthesis. They cannot photosynthesize in the presence of oxygen. They form pink, yellow, and purple 'blooms' in stagnant ponds, mud, and salt water pools, and are stimulated by the presence of sewage.

There are three groups: green sulphur bacteria and purple sulphur bacteria use hydrogen sulphide as their hydrogen source, purple non-sulphur bacteria use small organic compounds such as ethanol as their hydrogen source.

7 Cyanobacteria

These are blue–green aerobic bacteria which contain chlorophyll *a* and phycobilin pigments. They photosynthesize, using water and evolving oxygen, as green plants do, but they respire only in the dark. Some are also able to fix atmospheric nitrogen.

There are two sorts of cyanobacteria: those with round cells (cocci) and those with filamentous forms. They are often found in symbiotic association with other organisms, for example in lichens. Many cyanobacteria contain gas vacuoles to help them float, and they also often form 'blooms' at the surface of lakes.

8 Prochlorophyta

This phylum has one genus, *Prochloron*, which lives only in association with sea-squirts. It is special because it is the only known prokaryote which contains chlorophyll *b* as well as chlorophyll *a* and carotenoid pigments. It photosynthesizes just like a eukaryotic chloroplast.

9 Chemoautotrophic bacteria

These bacteria do not require sunlight or a complex food source, but live on air, water, minerals, and a simple energy source such as methane or hydrogen sulphide. Their role in recycling elements into forms which other living things can use is ecologically crucial.

For example, the two-stage recycling of nitrogen involves *Nitrosomonas* and other bacteria which oxidize ammonia to nitrite, and *Nitrobacter* and other bacteria which oxidize nitrite to nitrate. Others include *Thiobacillus* which oxidizes sulphur compounds to sulphate, and *Methylomonas* and *Methylococcus* which oxidize methane and methanol.

Figure 35
Electronmicrograph of *Rhodomicrobium vannielli*, an anaerobic photosynthetic bacterium.

Figure 36
1 Photomicrograph of *Anabaena* sp. (× 500), a filamentous cyanobacterium.
2 Electronmicrograph of *Gloeocapsa* sp. (× 1000), a coccoid cyanobacterium.

Figure 37
Transmission electronmicrograph of *Prochloron* (× 6600).

Figure 38
Drawing of *Nitrobacter winogradskyi*.

35

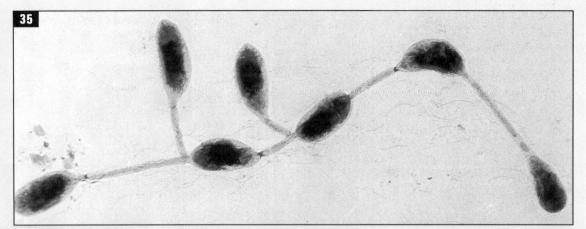

36 **1**

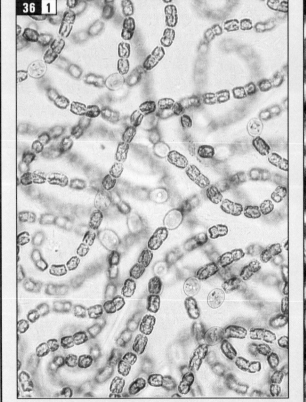

36 **2**

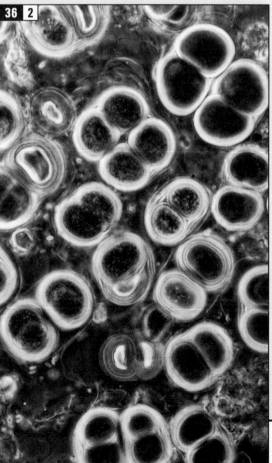

37

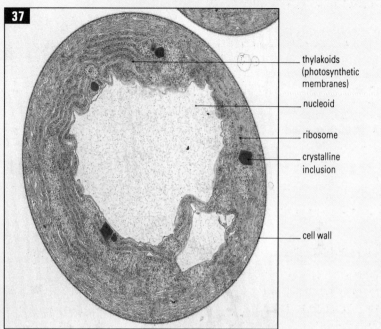

thylakoids
(photosynthetic
membranes)

nucleoid

ribosome

crystalline
inclusion

cell wall

38

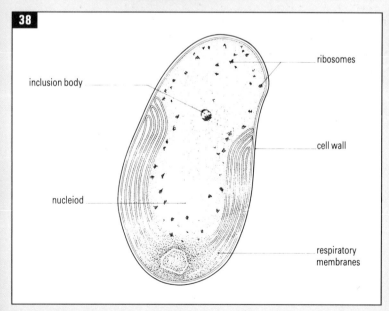

ribosomes

inclusion body

cell wall

nucleiod

respiratory
membranes

Respiring heterotrophs (groups 10 to 16)

10 Nitrogen-fixing bacteria

These transform atmospheric nitrogen into organic molecules. For example, *Rhizobium* which lives in association with legumes (plants of the pea family).

11 Pseudomonads

These are common and widespread bacteria which can metabolize many types of carbon compound. Some can respire anaerobically and some can live autotrophically if necessary, so they are very adaptable.

Pseudomonads cause many plant diseases including potato and tomato rot, peach blight, and soft rot of carrots.

12 Aeroendospora

These bacteria form resistant spores in their cells which can survive for years without water. Most are harmless.

The important genus *Bacillus* has over fifty species, most of which are harmless, although the spores are a nuisance in food preserving and other industries where sterile conditions are required. *B. anthracis* is a harmful one which causes anthrax. *B. subtilis* is found in dusty places everywhere.

13 Micrococci

This group includes *Staphylococcus* which causes mild food poisoning.

Figure 39
1 Root nodules which contain nitrogen-fixing bacteria on a runner bean.
2 Transmission electronmicrograph of five nitrogen-fixing bacteria, *Rhizobium leguminosarum* (× 15 000), in pea root.

Figure 40
1 Transmission electronmicrograph, shadow technique, of the soil bacterium *Pseudomonas fluorescens* (× 22 000).
2 Disease caused in tomatoes by *Pseudomonas* sp.

Figure 41
Drawing of *Bacillus* sp. containing a spore.

Figure 42
Polymorphonuclear leucocyte ingesting *Staphylococcus aureus* (× 15 500).

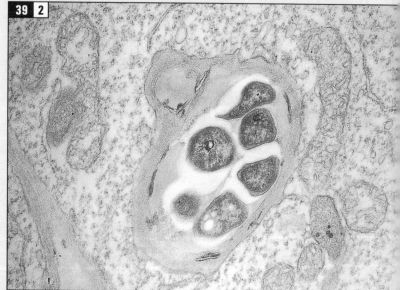

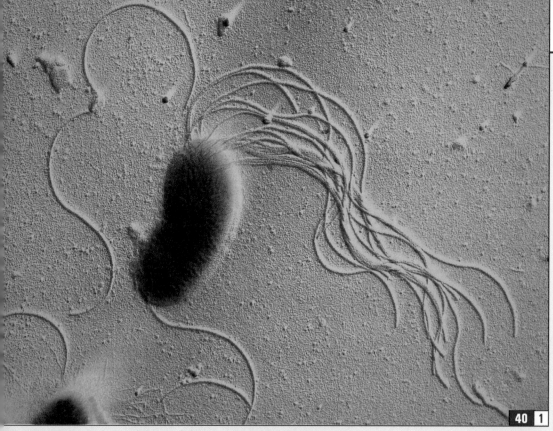

40 1

40 2

41

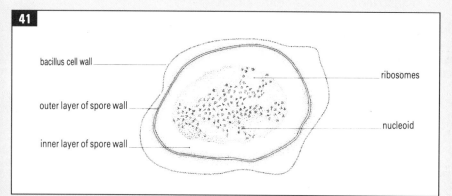

bacillus cell wall

ribosomes

outer layer of spore wall

nucleoid

inner layer of spore wall

42

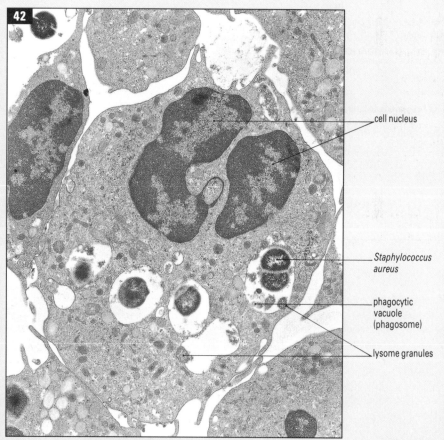

cell nucleus

Staphylococcus aureus

phagocytic vacuole (phagosome)

lysome granules

14 Omnibacteria (including Enterobacteria)

This is a huge group of bacteria. They are all aerobic and can respire anaerobically too if oxygen is short. Most are Gram-negative and of rod shape.

The group includes many famous bacteria which cause human diseases, all found in the gut. Examples are:

Genus	Disease caused
Salmonella	food poisoning and typhoid
Shigella	dysentery
Yersinia	plague
Vibrio	cholera

Escherichia coli is always found in digestive tracts and is a useful indicator of faecal pollution. Some strains cause diarrhoea. Others are widely used in laboratory experiments and some have been modified via DNA recombination to produce useful substances such as insulin and growth hormone.

15 Actinobacteria

These bacteria are filamentous and produce spores. *Streptomyces* are well known as a source of antibiotics. *Mycobacterium* species cause tuberculosis and leprosy.

16 Myxobacteria

These are gliding bacteria which form colonies in adverse conditions and produce a 'fruiting body' of resting bacterial cells.

Figure 43
1 Scanning electronmicrograph of *Salmonella typhi* (× 10 000), which causes typhoid.
2 Scanning electronmicrograph of *Vibrio cholerae* (× 10 000), which causes cholera.

Figure 44
1 Colonies of *Streptomyces glaucescens* growing on an agar plate.
2 Scanning electronmicrograph of young hyphae of *Streptomyces lividans* (× 240 000).
3 Scanning electronmicrograph of *Streptomyces lividans* showing immature and mature spore chains (× 750 000).

Figure 45
Myxococcus xanthus growing on an agar plate with a strain of *Escherichia coli* as substrate, after five hours . Migrating waves of vegetative cells and accumulations into fruiting bodies are shown.

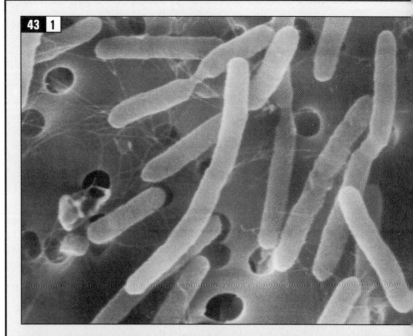

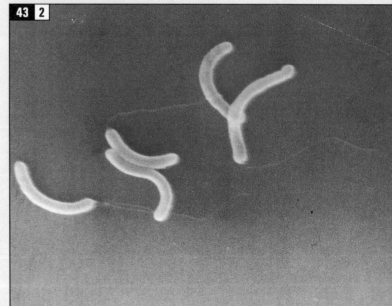

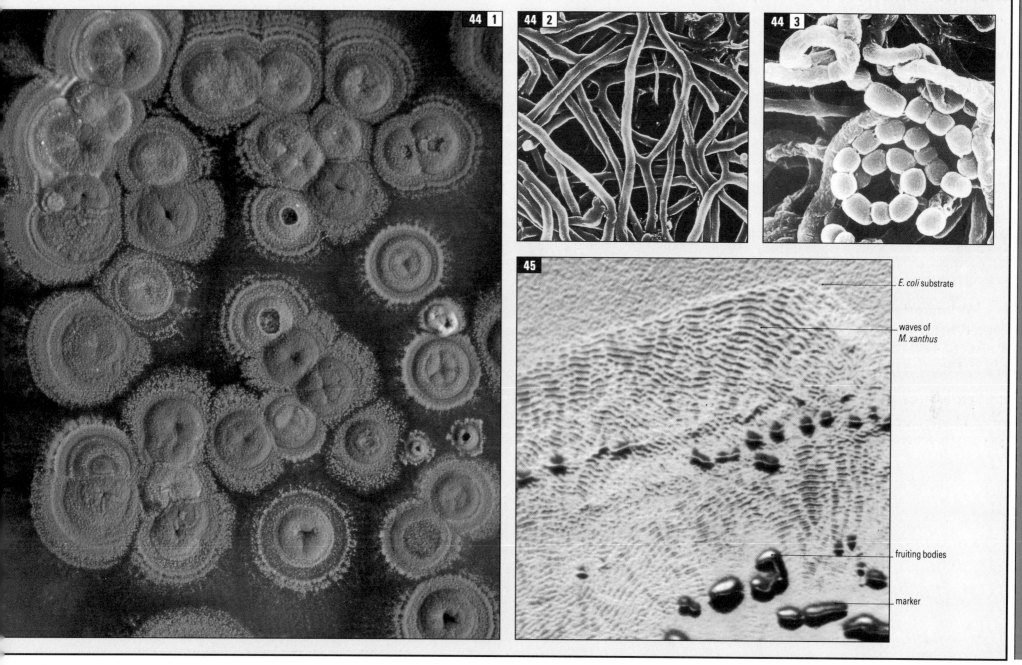

44 **1**

44 **2**

44 **3**

45

E. coli substrate

waves of
M. xanthus

fruiting bodies

marker

KINGDOM PROTISTA

Protista are eukaryotes and share eukaryotic features (see table 8). They are found in a wide range of habitats. They all require water for active growth.

The group contains single-celled eukaryotes and multicellular organisms which are closely related to them. It includes the algae, protozoa, and those fungi which have flagella (see figure 46). These are very diverse organisms, but are assembled together on the basis of their relatively simple level of organisation (see page 32).

Of the 27 protist phyla distinguished by Margulis and Barnes, 11 of the more familiar ones are outlined here.

1 Phylum Dinoflagellata

There are several thousands of species of these single-celled protists. Many are planktonic and marine. Some are photosynthetic, having chlorophylls *a* and *c*, and carotene and xanthophyll pigments. Some are parasitic and others are phagotrophic. All have two flagella, one of which fits in a transverse groove around the body, while the other trails behind. Many are rigid, because of plates of cellulose deposited under the plasma membrane. They reproduce by longitudinal cell division.

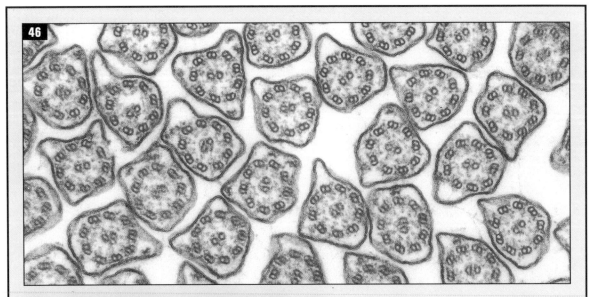

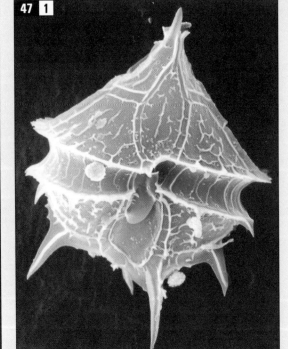

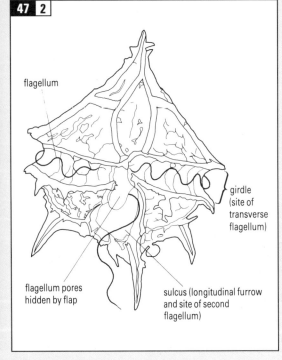

flagellum

girdle (site of transverse flagellum)

flagellum pores hidden by flap

sulcus (longitudinal furrow and site of second flagellum)

Figure 46
Electronmicrograph of transverse sections of eukaryote flagella (× 75 000), showing the characteristic 9 + 2 arrangement of microtubules.

Figure 47
1 Scanning electronmicrograph of the dinoflagellate *Peridinium quinquecorne* (× 3000).
2 Explanatory drawing of figure 1.

Some genera are luminescent, for example *Noctiluca*. Some dinoflagellates produce powerful poisons and are the cause of lethal 'red tides' when blooms of vast numbers of individuals colour the sea and poison fish and shellfish.

2 Phylum Chrysophyta

These are also known as golden–yellow algae. Many contain chlorophylls *a* and *c* plus carotenoid and xanthophyll pigments. Others have no chloroplasts and feed heterotrophically. They store oil as well as carbohydrate as a food reserve. They reproduce asexually, and many form siliceous cysts.

Most chryosophyta are minute. Most are freshwater forms, and some form large, complex colonies.

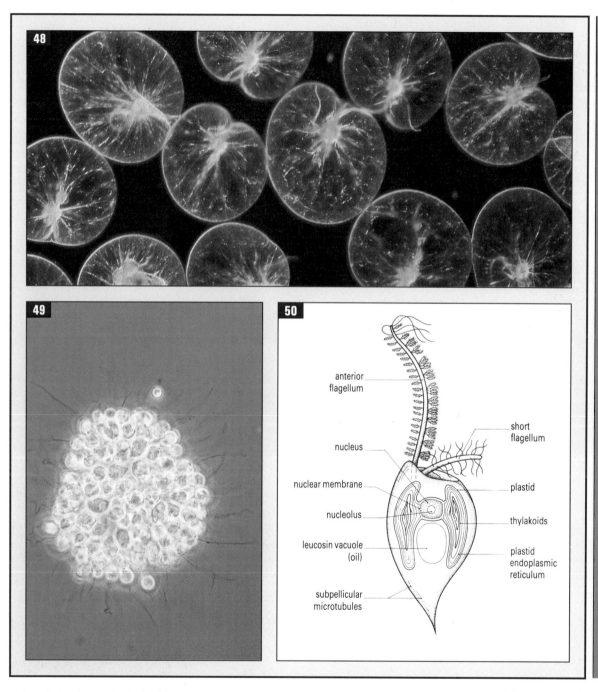

Figure 48
Noctiluca scintillans (× 50), a luminescent dinoflagellate. The picture shows part of a swarm from the sea surface.

Figure 49
A chrysophyte colony, *Synura* sp. (× 500).

Figure 50
Drawing of a single-celled chrysophyte showing unequal flagella.

3 Phylum Bacillariophyta (Diatoms)

Diatoms are single-celled protists which have beautiful two-valve tests (frustules) made of silica. These fit together like a pill box. They contain brownish plastids with chlorophyll *a* and *c*, carotenes and xanthophyll pigments (in particular fucoxanthin). They store oil as a food reserve. They have a sexual method of reproduction as well as an asexual one.

Diatoms occur in very large numbers and are the basis of many freshwater and seawater food chains. The accumulated shells of diatoms which have collected over millions of years form a fine, crumbly earth, diatomite. This is used under the name of kieselguhr as a fine abrasive powder.

4 Phylum Euglenophyta

These are single-celled organisms and many have chloroplasts containing chlorophylls *a* and *b*, carotene and xanthophyll pigments. Their food reserve is a special carbohydrate called paramylon. Euglenophyta have no cell walls but are covered with a pellicle made of protein and they move by the use of one or two conspicuous long flagella. They reproduce asexually.

5 Phylum Phaeophyta

These are the brown algae which are obvious on intertidal rocky seashores. They are all multicellular and many show a considerable degree of tissue differentiation.

The colour of brown algae is produced by the pigment fucoxanthin which masks the chlorophylls *a* and *c* and carotene pigments which they also contain. Phaeophyta store a carbohydrate food reserve called laminarin. They reproduce sexually and many have an alternation of haploid and diploid generations.

Alginic acids extracted from brown algae are non-toxic substances which are viscous and readily form gels. They are used widely in the food industry in the production of creams, ice creams, and sweets.

Figure 51
Diatom *Stephanodiscus astrea* (× 4000).

Figure 52
Euglena sp. (× 1000).

Figure 53
Fucus vesiculosus, bladder wrack.

Figure 54
Life cycle of *Laminaria*. Like many of the brown algae, *Laminaria* has an alternation of generations in which the conspicuous generation is the sporophyte. The gametophytes are small and inconspicuous.

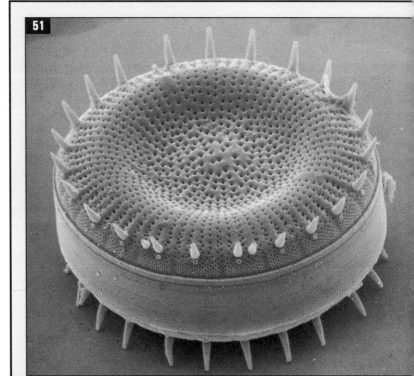

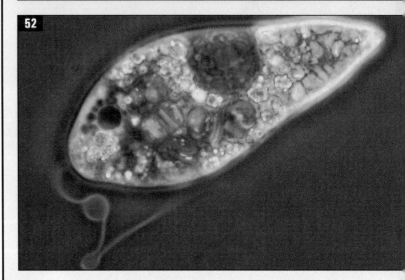

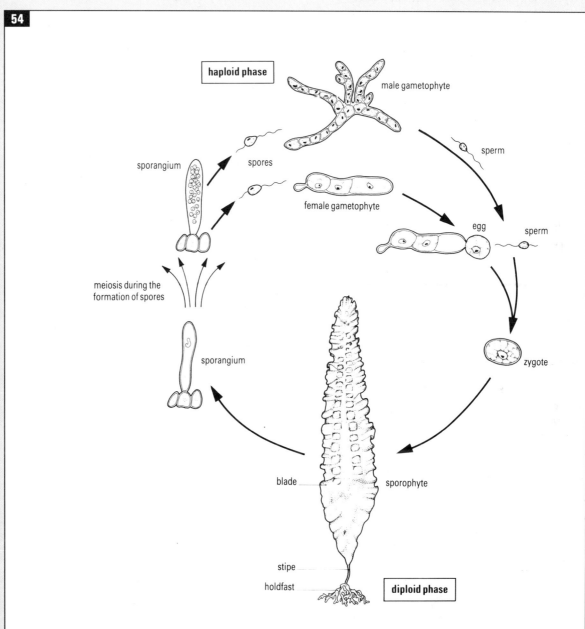

53

54

haploid phase

male gametophyte

sperm

sporangium

spores

sperm

female gametophyte

egg

zygote

meiosis during the
formation of spores

sporangium

blade

sporophyte

stipe

holdfast

diploid phase

6 Phylum Rhodophyta

The red algae are mainly marine. Their colour is produced by phycobilin pigments which are suitable for absorbing the light wavelengths which penetrate deep water. They also contain chlorophyll *a*, carotene and xanthophyll pigments. They store a carbohydrate food reserve called floridean starch. Rhodophyta are branched filaments or complex aggregations of filaments which give the appearance of flat sheets of cells. Rhodophyta have elaborate life histories, usually with alternation of generations. They never have flagella, and they have no motile gametes or spores.

Some Rhodophyta become encrusted with calcium carbonate. These are the 'coralline' algae. Agar is extracted from Rhodophyta.

7 Phylum Chlorophyta

The green algae are similar to plants in several important characteristics. They contain chlorophylls *a* and *b*, carotenes and xanthophylls, they store starch and they have cellulose cell walls. Most chlorophyta are aquatic, mainly freshwater. They may be single-celled, colonial, filamentous, or have a flattened appearance (this type of body is called a thallus, *Ulva* is an example). Chlorophyta usually reproduce sexually and they exhibit a great variety of life histories. Chlorophyte gametes and spores usually have two flagella.

Spirogyra, desmids, and other green algae that reproduce sexually by conjugation and which have no flagella, are grouped together as the class Conjugatophyceae.

Figure 55
Rhodymenia palmata, dulse, underwater in a pool.

Figure 56
Chlamydomonas sp. (× 400), a single-celled alga.

Figure 57
Volvox sp., a colonial form.

Figure 58
The life cycle of sea lettuce, *Ulva lactuca*. This shows an alternation of haploid (gametophyte) and diploid (sporophyte) generations. The two generations are indistinguishable, except for their reproductive structures.

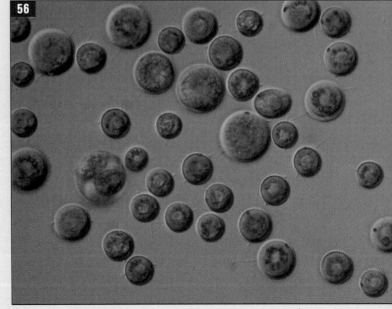

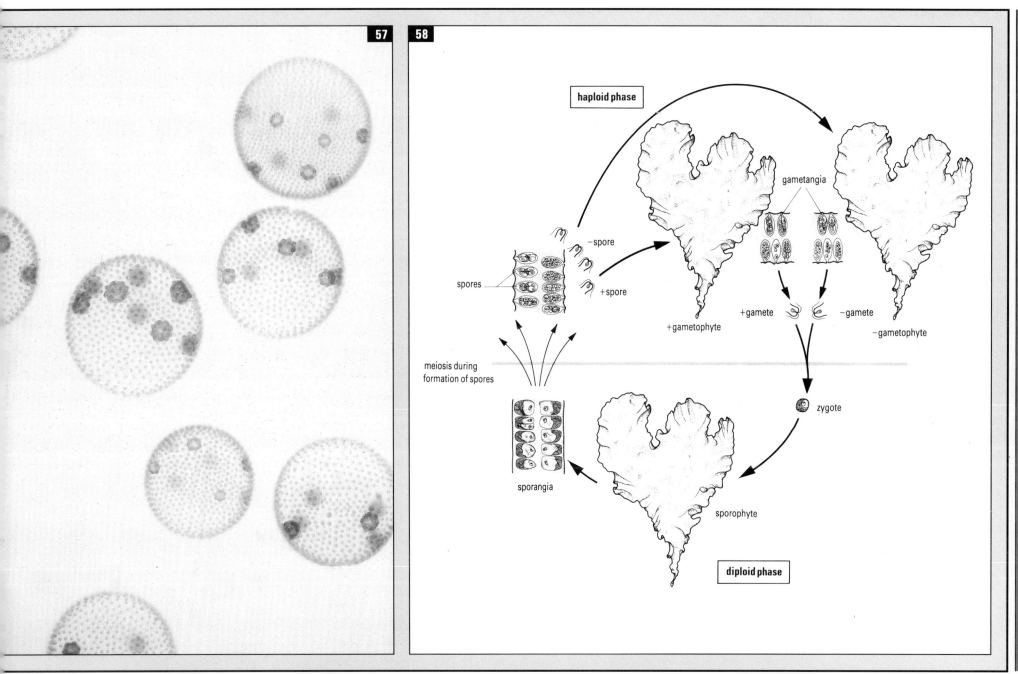

57

58

haploid phase

gametangia

−spore

+spore

spores

+gametophyte

+gamete

−gamete

−gametophyte

meiosis during
formation of spores

zygote

sporangia

sporophyte

diploid phase

8 Phylum Sarcodina

These are protists which are able to move and feed by producing outpushings of the cell called pseudopodia. There are about 16000 living species and many more are known as fossils. Together they show a great variety of form and the classification of this group is very complicated. Only two of the many groups are mentioned here.

Class Lobosea

These are single-celled amoeboid organisms. They are heterotrophic and widespread in soil and water; some are parasitic. Most lack flagella, but some may have a flagellated stage in the life cycle. Some have tests. They reproduce by simple division.

Parasitic amoebae, such as *Entamoeba histolytica* which causes dysentery, form cysts which resist digestion by their host.

Class Granuloreticulosea (figure 61)

These are single-celled, heterotrophic marine protists found floating in plankton, attached to other organisms and in the sand. Most of them are known as foraminifera. They have chalky tests full of holes through which cytoplasmic projections protrude. These cytoplasmic projections have a granular appearance. They have complicated life cycles with alternation of diploid and haploid generations. Fossil foraminifera are very common and very important for dating and correlating sedimentary rocks. Slime moulds (Myxomycota) are sometimes classified as protists in the phylum Sarcodina because they move by an ebb and flow of cytoplasm.

9 Phylum Ciliophora

Ciliophora are heterotrophic protists which are covered in short, flexible flagella called cilia used for fast swimming and food collecting. They are also identified by the possession of two nuclei in each cell, a macronucleus and a micronucleus. (See figures 62 and 63.)

Figure 59
Amoeba sp. (× 100).

Figure 60
Entamoeba histolytica (× 2500) containing red blood cells.

Figure 61
Globigerina sp. (× 250).

Figure 62
Paramecium sp. (× 1400).

Figure 63
Vorticella sp. (× 1200) lives attached to a substrate by a stalk.

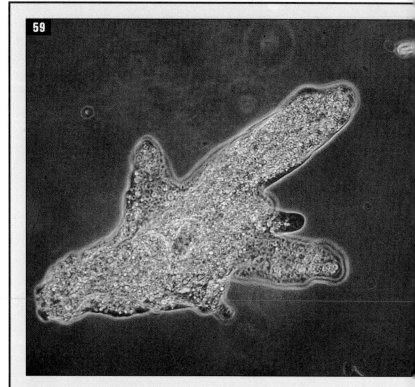

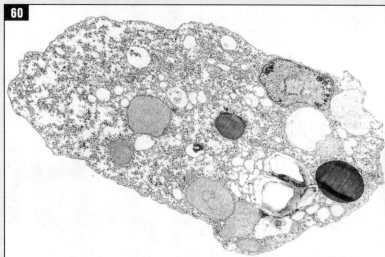

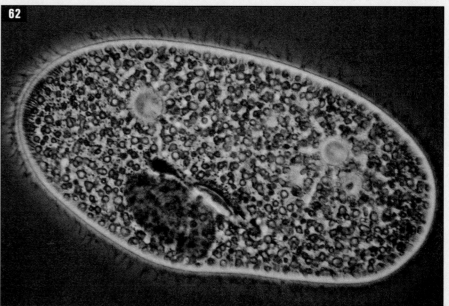

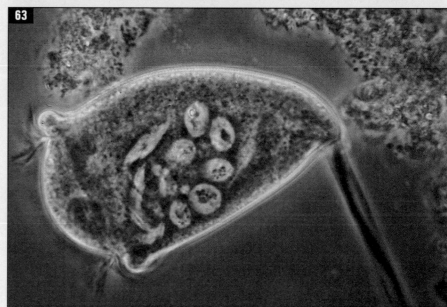

10 Phylum Apicomplexa

These protists are all spore-forming parasites of animals. They have complex life cycles which may involve several host species.

Plasmodium sp., malarial parasites which are transmitted to humans by the anopheline mosquito, are the most familiar members of this phylum.

11 Phylum Zoomastigina

These are heterotrophic single-celled protists which have one or more long flagella. They may be free living or parasitic.

The group includes *Trypanosoma*, the cause of African sleeping sickness, which is transmitted by the tsetse fly.

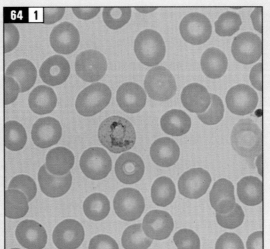
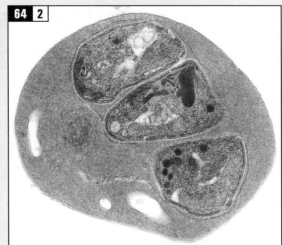

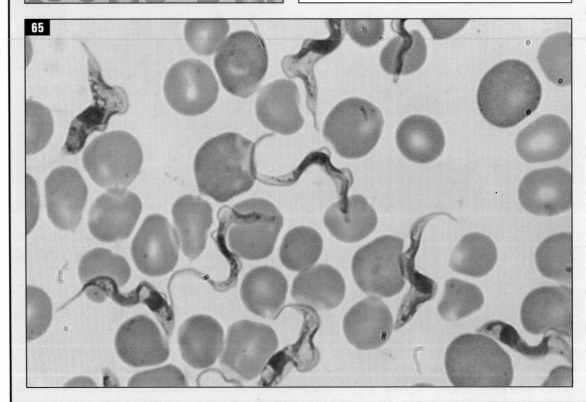

Figure 64
1 *Plasmodium vivax* (× 600), the late signet-ring stage in a red blood cell.
2 *Plasmodium falciparum* (× 15 000) merozoites in human red blood cell.

Figure 65
Trypanosoma sp. (× 2000) in human red blood smear.

KINGDOM PLANTAE

All plants are multicellular eukaryotes. They share the following features:

photosynthetic nutrition
chlorophylls *a* and *b*, xanthophyll and carotenoid pigments
cellulose cell walls
development from multicellular diploid embryos which are nourished by special tissue
life histories which involve two generations: a diploid generation,

the sporophyte (phase during which spores are produced), and a haploid generation, the gametophyte (phase during which sex cells are produced); the two generations alternate with each other.

A classification of the plant kingdom is given in table 10.
Some of these plant groupings contain only a few species or relatively uncommon ones. Further details have been given only of the larger groups and those containing the more familiar species.

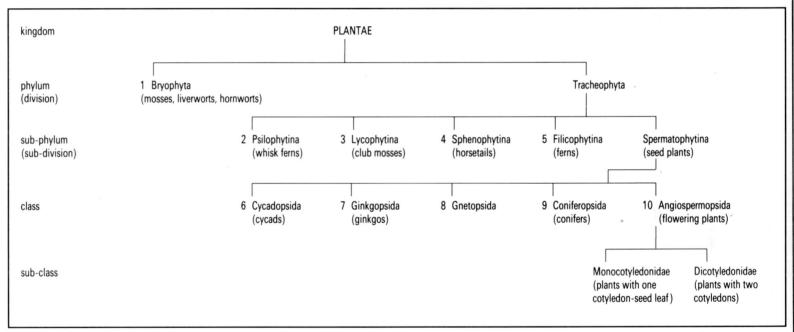

This classification retains the traditional groupings for 'plants with conducting vessels' (tracheophytes) and for 'seed plants' (spermatophytes). Groups 2, 3, 4 and 5 are sometimes grouped together as 'pteridophytes'. Groups 6, 7, 8 and 9 are sometimes grouped together as 'gymnosperms' (plants with naked seeds).

Table 10
A classification of the plant kingdom, after Stace, 1980.

1 Bryophyta

Bryophytes are distinguished from other plant groups by their lack of xylem and phloem and by their distinctive life history (figure 66). They are largely restricted to damp places, as they require a film of water for fertilization and many have poorly developed mechanisms for water conservation. The familiar green moss or liverwort 'plant' is the gametophyte phase (figure 67).

Tracheophyta

All the remaining plant groups which have xylem and phloem are tracheophytes. They are well suited for life on land, having true roots and leaves covered with a waxy cuticle. The familiar green plant is the sporophyte phase.

2 Psilophytina
3 Lycophytina
4 Sphenophytina

Sub-divisions 2, 3, and 4 (whisk ferns, club mosses, and horsetails) include relatively few living species. Club mosses and horsetails up to 40 m high, together with tree ferns, dominated the forests of the Carboniferous period and were the chief coal-forming plants. Their small relatives have survived to modern times.

Figure 66
The life cycle of a moss.

Figure 67
A variety of bryophytes. Liverworts are sometimes 'leafy', if so their leaves *appear* to be in pairs.
1   A moss, *Bryum capillare*.
2   A liverwort, *Pellia epiphylla*.
3   A leafy liverwort, *Diplophyllum albicans*.
4   A cushion moss: white moss, *Leucobryum glaucum*, on beech wood floor.

Figure 68
1   Stag's horn club moss, *Lycopodium clavatum* (Lycophytina).
2   Horsetail, *Equisetum* (Sphenophytina).
3   Tree fern, *Alsophila capensis* (Filicophytina).

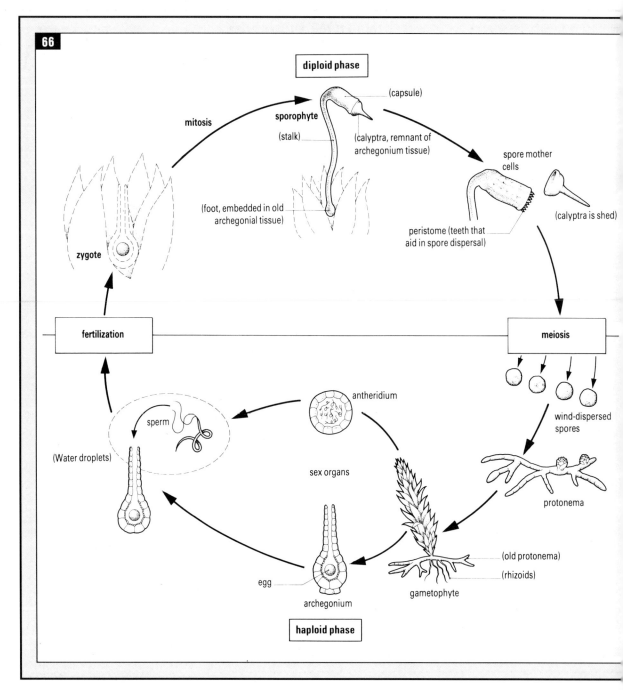

67 | 1

persistent — diploid sporophyte

leaves spirally arranged — haploid gametophyte

grows in damp places

67 | 2

spore capsule splits into four — diploid sporophyte

short-lived

usually a flattened thallus — haploid gametophyte

grows in damp places

67 | 3

67 | 4

68 | 1

68 | 2

68 | 3

5 Filicophytina

The absence of seeds and the existence of a free living photosynthetic gametophyte stage, which remains dependent on water to allow fertilization to occur, distinguish ferns from spermatophytes.

Spermatophytina

All the remaining plant groups bear seeds. The haploid gametophyte is very much reduced and develops in specialized reproductive structures (cones or flowers) which are borne on the sporophyte.

6 Cycadopsida
7 Ginkgopsida
8 Gnetopsida

Classes 6, 7, and 8 (Cycadopsida, Ginkgopsida, and Gnetopsida) are represented by few present day species, but cycads and ginkgos were important in the Mesozoic era.

9 Coniferopsida

The distinctive feature of conifers is the presence of male and female cones, often both on the same plant. Waxy, needle-shaped leaves are another familiar characteristic. Their seeds are not enclosed by an ovary wall as they are in the angiosperms.

Figure 69
A fern showing the characteristic features of Filicophytina.

Figure 70
1   The alternating generations of a fern: first leaf (sporophyte) growing from prothallus (gametophyte).
2   The life cycle of a fern.

Figure 71
1   Cycad, *Encephalartos friderici-quilielmi*, showing old male cones and new leaf growth from centre.
2   Maidenhair tree, *Gingko biloba*, the only living member of this group.
3   Female and male branches of *Gingko biloba*.

Figure 72
1   Scots pine, *Pinus sylvestris*.
2   The life cycle of a conifer.

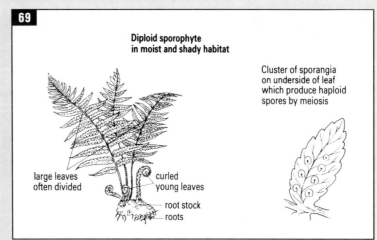

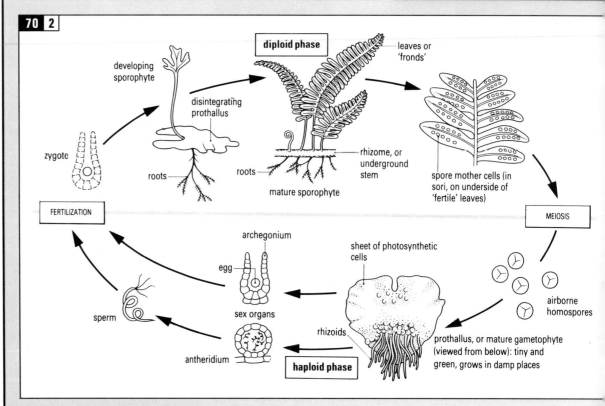

71 1

71 2

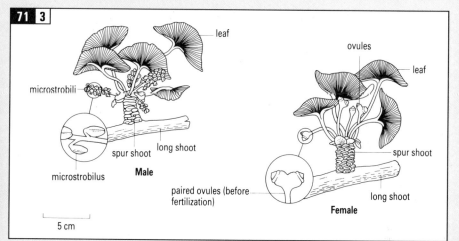

71 3

leaf

microstrobili

microstrobilus

spur shoot

long shoot

Male

5 cm

ovules

leaf

spur shoot

paired ovules (before fertilization)

long shoot

Female

72 1

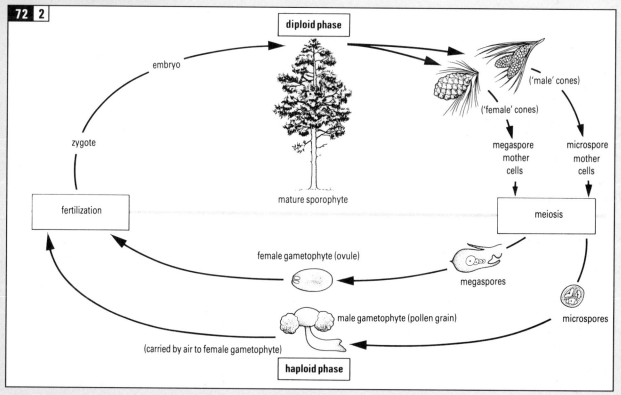

72 2

diploid phase

embryo

zygote

('male' cones)

('female' cones)

megaspore mother cells

microspore mother cells

mature sporophyte

fertilization

meiosis

female gametophyte (ovule)

megaspores

male gametophyte (pollen grain)

microspores

(carried by air to female gametophyte)

haploid phase

10 Angiospermopsida

This group includes all the familiar flowering plants. Apart from having flowers, the other distinctive feature of angiosperms is that their seeds develop inside an ovary.

Angiosperms are divided into two sub-classes on the basis of the number of cotyledons (seed leaves) which they have. Monocotyledons have one cotyledon, dicotyledons have two.

There are other differences between the two groups, some of which may be seen in figure 75.

The flower is unique to angiosperms. Flowers have made possible the development of an infinite variety of mechanisms which involve outside agencies such as insects, birds, wind, water, and mammals in the transfer of pollen and dispersal of seeds.

The angiosperms are the overwhelmingly dominant plant group. They include all our major food plants, and we are totally dependent on them.

Figure 73
The life cycle of a flowering plant.

Figure 74
1 Longitudinal section of a monocotyledonous seed, *Triticum* embryo.
2 Longitudinal section of a dicotyledonous seed, *Capsella*.

Figure 75
1 Cock's foot grass, *Dactylis glomerata*.
2 Sweetcorn, *Zea mays*.
3 Tulip, *Tulipa gretgii*.
4 English elm, *Ulmus procera*.
5 Close-up of tomato flower truss.
6 Dog rose, *Rosa canina*.
7 Water lily, *Nymphaea*.
8 Ripening tomato fruit.
9 Meadow buttercups, *Ranunculus acris*.

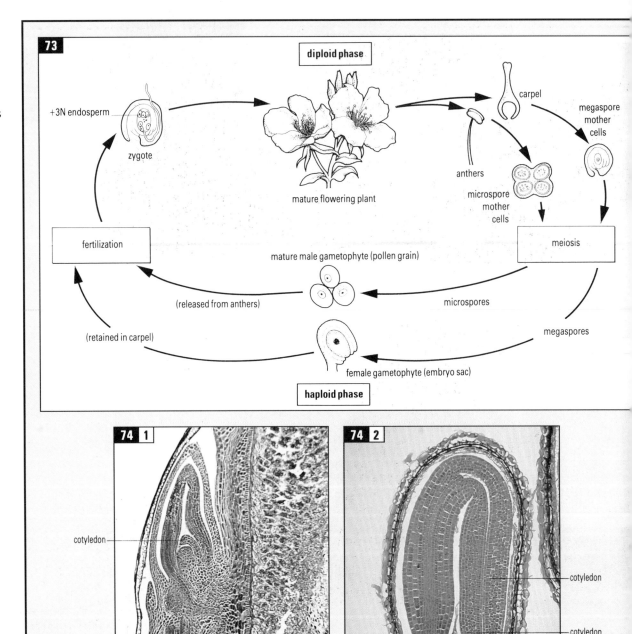

KINGDOM FUNGI

Table 11
A classification of the fungi, after Margulis, 1982.

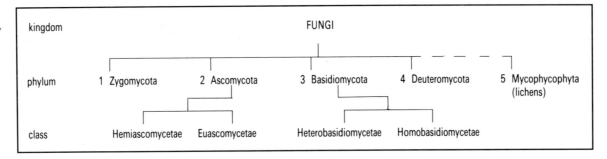

The fungi are eukaryotic, multicellular or multinucleate organisms. The features they share are:

cell walls which usually contain chitin

lack of chlorophyll

aerobic respiration (normally)

need for damp conditions

that they consist of thread-like filaments (hyphae) which may be divided into short sections by cross walls (septa); the mass of hyphae which constitutes the 'body' of a fungus is called a mycelium

a parasitic, mutualistic, or saprotrophic (secreting enzymes onto food and absorbing the products of this external digestion) mode of life

an asexual method of reproduction by spores; although most are known to have a sexual method of reproduction as well

lack of flagella at any stage of the life cycle

Table 11 shows a classification of the fungi.

1 Phylum Zygomycota

Zygomycote fungal hyphae normally lack cross walls. The zygospore, from which this group is named, is a resistant spore produced after sexual conjugation between two compatible hyphae.

There are three sub-groups of Zygomycota: the orders Mucorales, Entomophthorales, and Zoopagales.

Saprotrophic fungi of the Mucorales are widespread in soil and dung, and are common food spoiling organisms. *Mucor, Phycomyces,* and *Rhizopus* are examples of this group. *Rhizopus stolonifer,* the black bread mould, also spoils strawberries and peaches. Other *Rhizopus* species are used to ferment soya beans in the production of various oriental foods.

Members of the two other orders of Zygomycota are parasites of amoebae, nematodes, and insects (and of Mucorales!).

Figure 76
Mucor mycelium on bread ($\times$ 40).

Figure 77
Rhizopus sp. showing release of asexual spores.

Figure 78
Conjugation in *Rhizopus*:
1   Nuclei from the two haploid hyphae will fuse together in pairs.
2   The zygospore forms a thick resistant wall.
3   After a dormant period meiosis occurs and a haploid hypha grows from the spore. This normally produces a sporangium that releases large numbers of haploid spores.

Figure 79
Scanning electronmicrograph of *Rhizopus sexualis* which shows a zygospore developing between two suspensor cells ($\times$ 600).

76

77

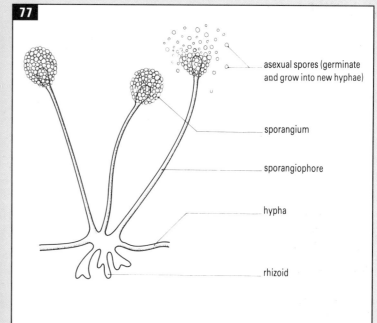

asexual spores (germinate and grow into new hyphae)

sporangium

sporangiophore

hypha

rhizoid

78 **1**

'plus' hypha
'minus' hypha

conjugating hyphae

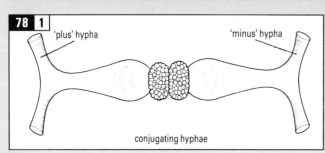

78 **2**

zygospore in zygosporangium

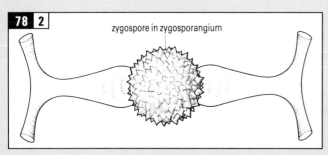

78 **3**

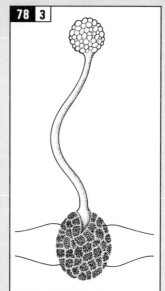

79

2 Phylum Ascomycota

This Phylum includes yeasts, cup fungi, morels, truffles, and powdery mildews. The characteristic feature of the group is the sac-like ascus. Following sexual conjugation and fusion of the nuclei of two mating types, meiosis produces four haploid nuclei which typically divide by mitosis to produce eight ascospores inside an ascus. Ascomycota also reproduce asexually, by fission, budding, or asexual spores.

Ascomycota have septate hyphae, with pores in the septa which potentially allow cytoplasmic continuity between all parts of the mycelium.

There are four classes of Ascomycota, two of which are the Hemiascomycetae and the Euascomycetae.

Class Hemiascomycetae
This group produces asci which are not enclosed in an ascocarp. It includes yeasts, which are single-celled microscopic fungi. Conjugation between two yeast cells is followed by the formation of an ascus usually containing four ascopores.

Figure 80

1 The life cycle of an ascomycote. A monokaryotic cell contains one haploid nucleus. A dikaryotic cell contains two haploid nuclei, one of each mating type. When the two nuclei fuse they form a diploid nucleus.

2 Ascocarp with asci and spores of *Peziza* (× 500).

Figure 81

Electronmicrograph of a longitudinal section through vegetative hypha of *Pyronema domesticum*, showing septum, open pore, and numerous mitochondria (× 43 200).

Figure 82

Electronmicrograph of a section of tetrad of yeast ascospores, *Saccharomyces cerevisiae* (× 23 000).

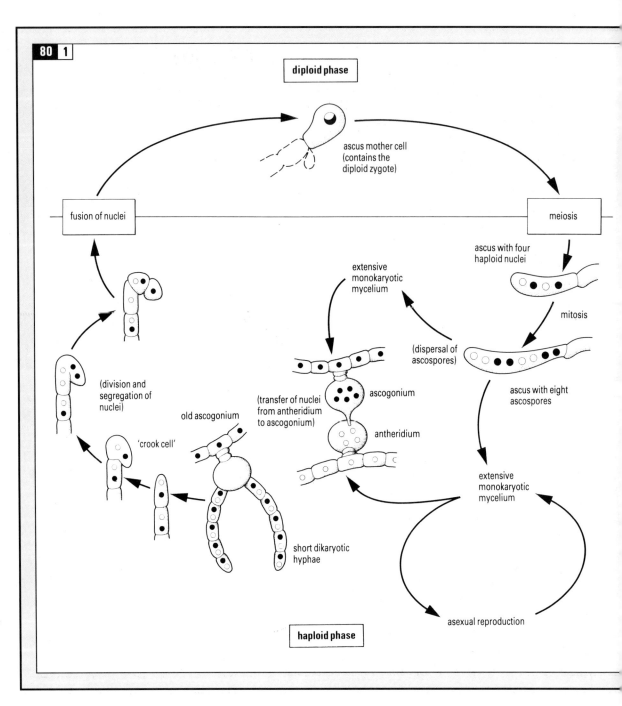

80 1

diploid phase

ascus mother cell
(contains the diploid zygote)

fusion of nuclei

meiosis

ascus with four haploid nuclei

extensive monokaryotic mycelium

mitosis

(dispersal of ascospores)

(division and segregation of nuclei)

(transfer of nuclei from antheridium to ascogonium)

ascogonium

old ascogonium

antheridium

'crook cell'

ascus with eight ascospores

extensive monokaryotic mycelium

short dikaryotic hyphae

asexual reproduction

haploid phase

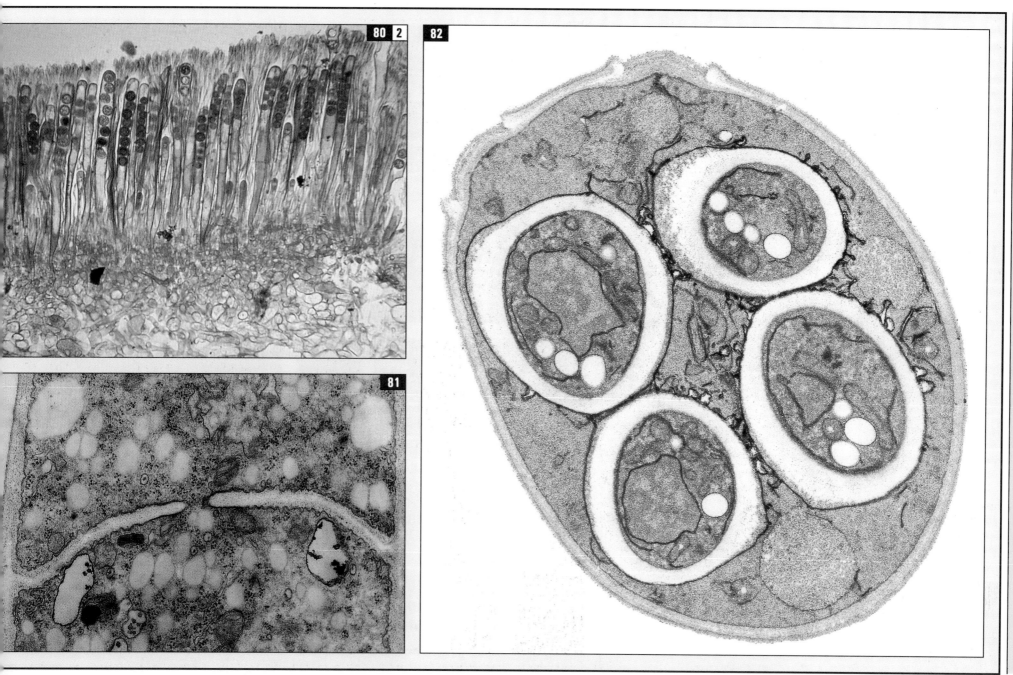

Class Euascomycetae

Euascomycete asci develop within a surrounding ascocarp. There are nineteen orders in this class, including those illustrated in figure 83.

Ascomycota cause many diseases of plants, including leaf spots, corn ear rot, apple scab, brown rots, and leaf curls. Some are useful, yeasts being outstandingly so in baking, brewing, as a food supplement high in vitamins, and as producers of ethanol, proteins, vitamins, and enzymes in industrial processes.

3 Phylum Basidiomycota

This phylum includes mushrooms, toadstools, puffballs, rusts, smuts, and bracket fungi. The unifying feature of this variable group is the basidium. Following sexual conjugation and fusion of the nuclei of the two mating types, the diploid nucleus divides by meiosis to produce four basidiospores.

Figure 83

Photographs of a range of Euascomycete fungi.
1 *Erysiphe graminis*, a powdery mildew, on wheat.
2 *Neurospora* sp., growing on an agar plate.
3 *Claviceps purpurea*, ergot, on wheat.
4 *Morchella* sp., morel.
5 *Tuber aestivum*, truffles.
6 Scanning electronmicrograph of the mycelium of *Ceraticystis ulmi* in elm wood (× 50), the cause of Dutch elm disease.

Figure 84

Part of a gill of *Coprinus disseminatus* (× 4000),
showing the basidia which bear four basidiospores.

Figure 85

1 *Coprinus lagopus* showing gills.
2 Vertical section through gills of *Coprinus* to show developing basidiospores.

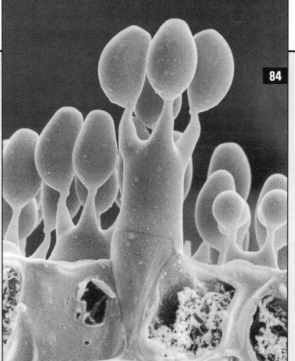

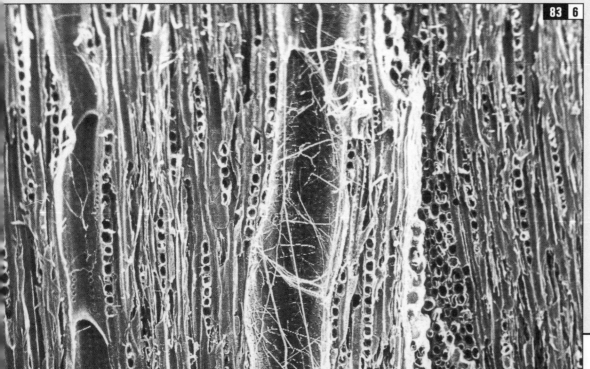

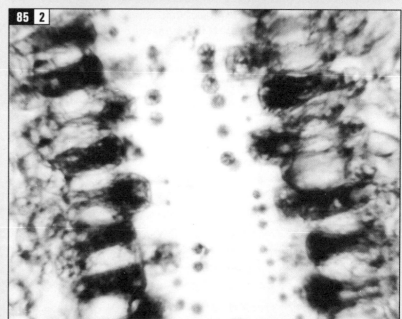

The familiar mushrooms and toadstools are the fruiting bodies, called basidiocarps, in which basidia are formed.

Many Basidiomycota (and some other fungi) form a close association with the roots of plants.

The fungus-root associations are called mycorrhizae. They benefit the plants by facilitating uptake of minerals, and the fungi by providing them with carbohydrates from the plant.

The phylum is divided into two classes: Heterobasidiomycetae (jelly fungi, rusts, and smuts), and Homobasidiomycetae (including bracket fungi, puffballs, and mushrooms).

4 Phylum Deuteromycota

This group is sometimes called Fungi Imperfecti. It is a collection of fungi for which a sexual stage has not been recognized. Since fungal classification is based on sexual reproductive structures (zygospores, asci, and basidia) the fungi lacking such structures are left out.

Penicillium and *Aspergillus* are here included in the Deuteromycota. *Penicillia* are moulds, typically green or blue, which cause soft rots of fruit. They also destroy leather and fabrics, but they do make good cheese (Camembert, Roquefort, and Gorgonzola) and they may be used industrially to produce penicillin. *Aspergillus flavus*, which grows on peanuts among other foods, produces a poisonous substance called aflatoxin.

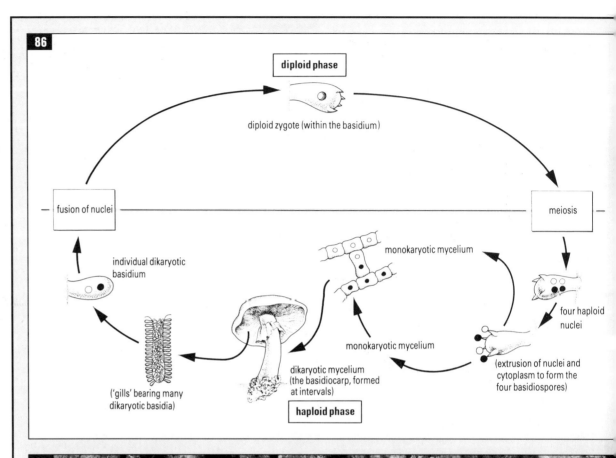

Figure 86
The life cycle of Basidiomycota.

Figure 87
Mycorrhizal roots of beech, exposed by pulling back the leaf mould on the floor of a beech wood.

Figure 88
Photographs of Basidiomycete fungi:
1 *Ustilago maydis*, on maize.
2 *Pleurotus ostreatus*, oyster mushrooms, growing on a beech tree.
3 *Lycoperdon* sp., puffball.
4 *Boletus badius*.
5 *Amanita muscaria*, fly agarics.

Figure 89
Penicillium sp. ($\times$ 500). Hyphae with several conidiophores bearing conidia (asexual spores).

88 1

88 2

88 3

88 4

88 5

89

5 Phylum Mycophycophyta

These are the lichens. A lichen is an association between an alga and a fungus (usually an ascomycote), each member of the partnership being dependent on the other. Lichens are often the first colonizers of bare rock, and their capacity to survive adverse conditions is well illustrated by the fact that hundreds of species are found in the Antarctic.

They reproduce by releasing soredia, small fragments of algae and fungi. They also form spores similar to those of non-lichen fungi.

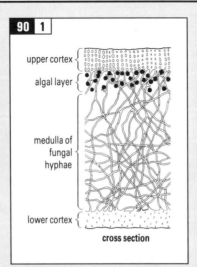

upper cortex

algal layer

medulla of fungal hyphae

lower cortex

cross section

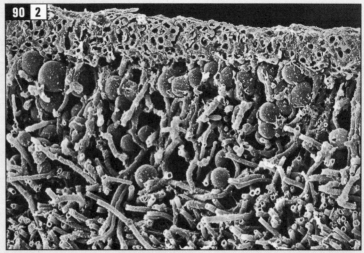

Figure 90
1 The structure of a lichen:
2 Electronmicrograph of a vertical section of thallus of the lichen, *Parmelia sulcata* (× 500).

Figure 91
Lichens on a rocky shore in Wales.

KINGDOM ANIMALIA

All animals are multicellular eukaryotes. The features they share are:

heterotrophic nutrition
lack of photosynthetic pigments
no cell walls
a high level of tissue differentiation with specialized body
    organs (most)

a sexual method of reproduction, the only haploid stage in the life
    cycle being in the production of eggs and sperms
division of the fertilized egg into a hollow ball of cells called a
    blastula

A classification of the animal kingdom is given in table 12.

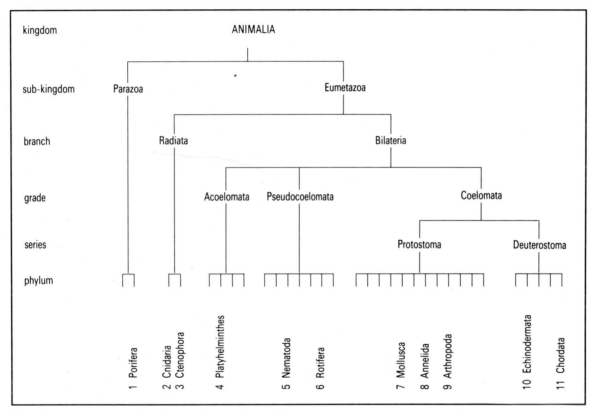

* Each line represents a phylum. Only the named phyla are discussed here.

Table 12
A classification of the animal kingdom.

Sub-kingdom Parazoa

These animals have a simple structure in which there is no organization of cells into tissues. They are of an indeterminate shape and have no nervous system.

1 Phylum Porifera

These are the sponges.

Sub-kingdom Eumetazoa

The body cells are interdependent and are organized into tissues and organs.

Branch Radiata

This consists of animals in which the body shows basic radial symmetry: that is, it could be divided along more than one plane passing through the centre to give equivalent, roughly equal halves (for example, a jellyfish).

2 Phylum Cnidaria

This phylum includes the least complex Eumetazoans. Two body forms exist: polyp and medusa (figure 94). Each has two distinct layers of cells (epidermis and gastrodermis) with a layer of jelly (mesoglea) in between which contains a network of nerve cells.
    The members of this phylum are divided into three classes.

Class Hydrozoa
These include *Hydra* and colonial hydroids. They display polypoid or medusoid forms or both.

Figure 92
Drawing of a sponge showing characteristic features. The body of a sponge consists of a collection of several types of cells with a jelly-like substance in between. The structure is supported by spicules of calcium or silica in the jelly (or by protein fibres, as in bath sponges). Food is extracted from water by the flagellated collar cells. There is no mouth or gut.

Figure 93
Brown sponge, *Hemectyon ferox*. Sponges are often brightly coloured with their own pigments and with those of symbiotic algae. Because of its simple structure, if a sponge is sieved the cells re-form after a time into a new individual.

Figure 94
The two body forms of *Cnidaria*: polyp and medusa. The mouth is the only opening to the body cavity.

Figure 95
Section through the body wall of a Cnidarian (*Hydra*) showing the two layers of cells.

Figure 96
Two examples of hydrozoans:
1 A solitary polyp, the freshwater *Hydra*. *Hydra* reproduces asexually by 'budding'. A bud which will eventually separate can be seen.
2 Portuguese man-of-war, *Physalia physalis*, eating a fish. *Physalia* is a colonial hydrozoan with polypoid and medusoid individuals. Each type has its own job in the colony: as a gas-filled float, catching prey, digestion, or reproduction.

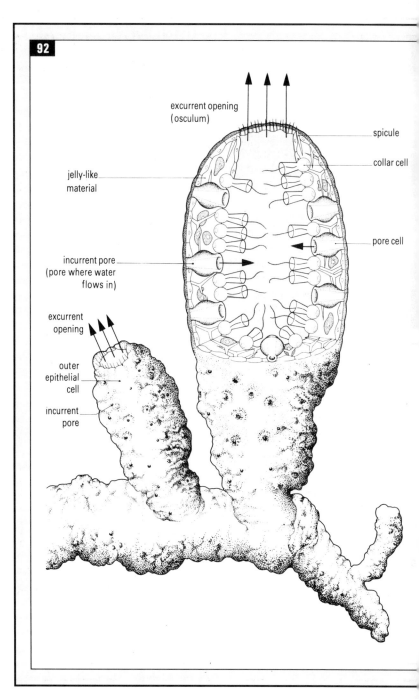

93

94

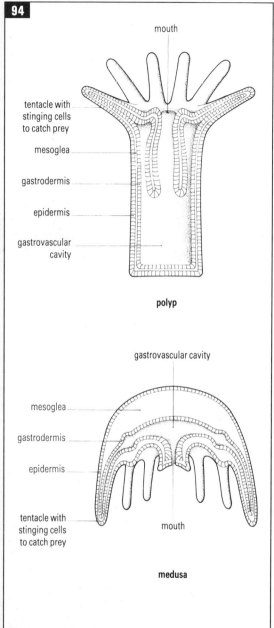

mouth

tentacle with
stinging cells
to catch prey

mesoglea

gastrodermis

epidermis

gastrovascular
cavity

polyp

gastrovascular cavity

mesoglea

gastrodermis

epidermis

tentacle with
stinging cells
to catch prey

mouth

medusa

96 **1**

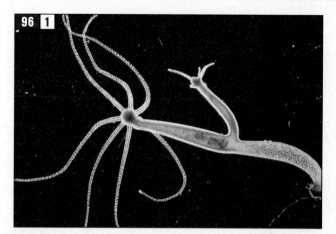

96 **2**

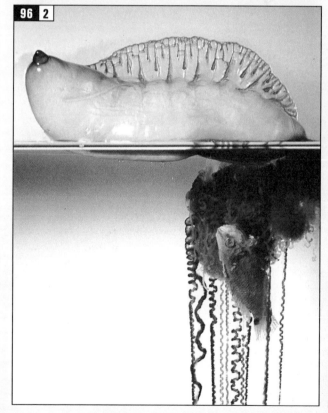

95

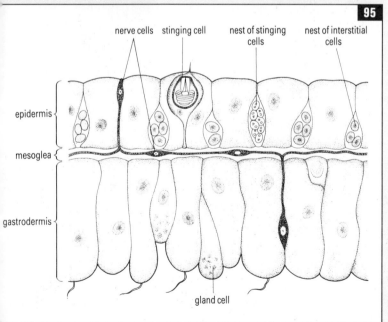

nerve cells   stinging cell   nest of stinging
cells

nest of interstitial
cells

epidermis

mesoglea

gastrodermis

gland cell

Class Scyphozoa

This is the class of true jellyfish. The medusa is the dominant individual; the polyp exists only as a larval stage.

Class Anthozoa

These are the sea anemones and corals. They have solitary or colonial polyp forms; medusoid forms are absent.

3 Phylum Ctenophora

This phylum consists of the comb jellies (sometimes called sea gooseberries).

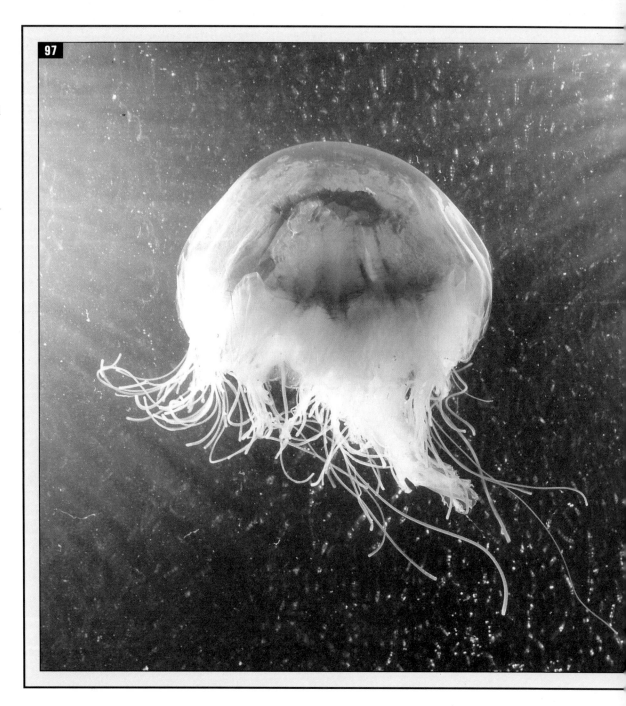

Figure 97

A scyphozoan, the violet jellyfish, *Cyanea lamarcki*, swimming. Compared with the hydrozoa, jellyfish have more mesoglea (which helps them to float), they are more active, and they have a more complex nerve net.

Figure 98

1 A coral reef. Reefs are formed from the 'skeleton' of the corals. They are the greatest constructions of the animal world. They consist of tonnes of calcium carbonate. They also provide a habitat for the most beautiful and varied forms of life.
2 A solitary anthozoan, a sea anemone, *Actinia equina fragacea* (the strawberry variety of Beadlet anemone) with one *A. equina* (brown).
3 Colonial anthozoans: polyps of sea whip coral. Corals rely on symbiotic algae which are necessary for the building of their skeletons. They are therefore only found in shallow, clear water where there is sunlight for photosynthesis.

Figure 99

Drawing of *Pleurobrachia pileus*. There are eight rows of cilia for swimming, but there are no stinging cells. Food is trapped with sticky lassoo cells on tentacles which are then wiped across the mouth.

Figure 100

Comb jelly (sea gooseberry), *Pleurobrachia pileus*.

98 1

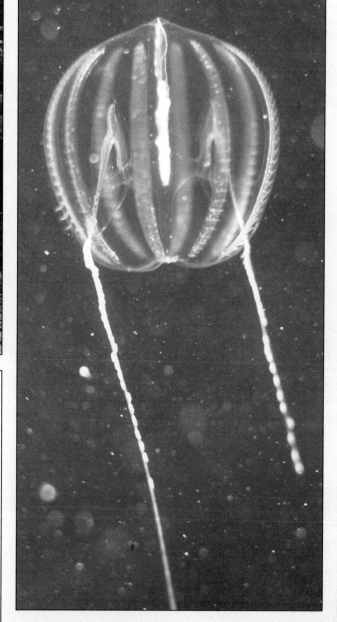

98 2

98 3

99

mouth

pharynx

cilia

tentacles

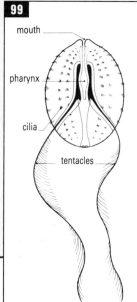

100

73

Branch Bilateria

Animals in this branch show bilateral symmetry: that is, there is only one plane which divides the organism into two equivalent halves. In this branch three body layers are formed as the embryo develops:

1 endoderm, from which most of the gut forms;
2 mesoderm, which gives rise to muscles, skeleton, and other internal organs and from which a body cavity called a coelom may form in which the organs are suspended;
3 ectoderm, from which the outer body covering, epidermis, and nervous system develop.

Bilaterally symmetrical animals are divided into three grades according to whether they have a coelom (figure 101).

Grade Acoelomata

No coelom is formed from the mesoderm.

4 Phylum Platyhelminthes (flatworms)

These are the simplest animals to have a well defined anterior end or 'head'. This phylum is divided into three classes.

Class Turbellaria
These are free living forms.

Class Trematoda
This class consists of the flukes, external and internal parasites whose life cycle involves an invertebrate and vertebrate host.

Class Cestoda
These are the tapeworms, internal parasites whose life cycle usually involves two vertebrate hosts.

Figure 101
Drawings showing the three grades of body plans of bilaterally symmetrical animals.

Figure 102
The body plan of a flatworm (planarian).

Figure 103
A free living freshwater flatworm, *Dendrocoelum lacteum*, crawling over a skeleton leaf under water. These flatworms have a ciliated epidermis and move by gliding. They are carnivores and scavengers.

Figure 104
Drawing of a typical life cycle of a fluke, *Schistosoma mansoni*, the parasite which causes the disease bilharzia in humans.

Figure 105
A tapeworm. Cestodes are specially adapted to live in guts. They are not digested by the host's enzymes; their 'heads' are modified for attachment to the wall of the gut; and they lack a gut themselves since they absorb digested food through their body surface. Their reproductive system is very well developed.

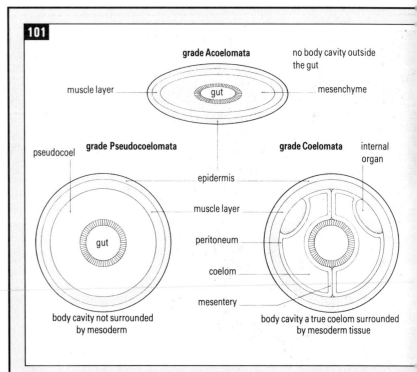

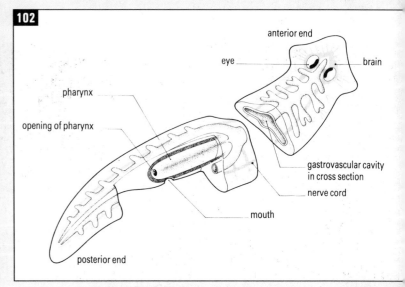

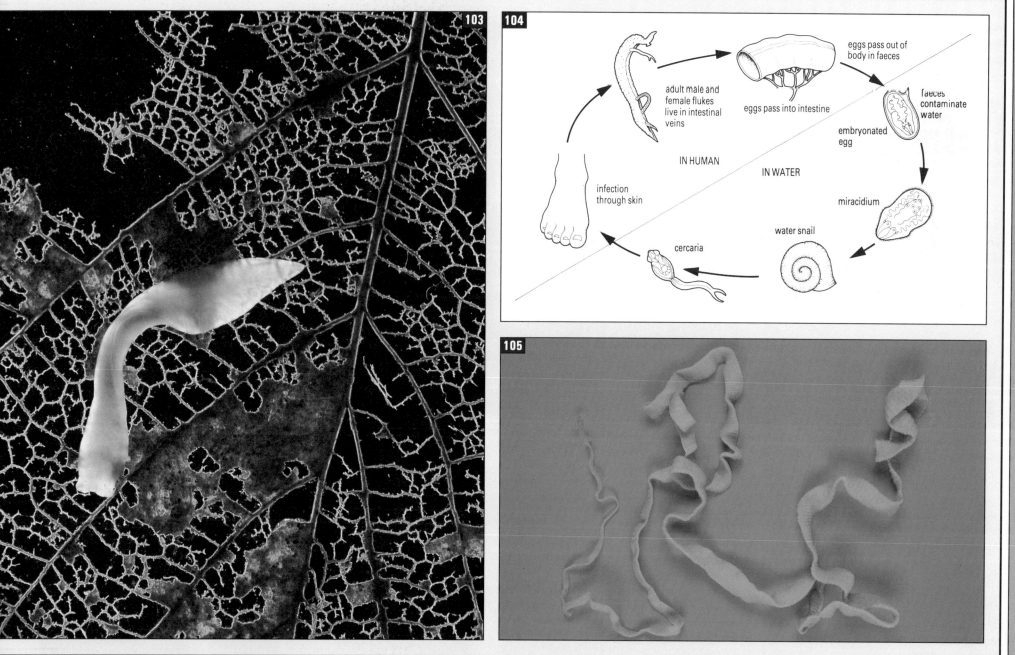

103

104

eggs pass out of body in faeces

adult male and female flukes live in intestinal veins

eggs pass into intestine

faeces contaminate water

embryonated egg

IN HUMAN

IN WATER

infection through skin

miracidium

cercaria

water snail

105

Grade Pseudocoelomata

5 Phylum Nematoda

This phylum is composed entirely of roundworms, which all look remarkably alike. They are inconspicuous but extremely numerous and are found as free living forms in water and soil and as parasites in plants and animals. The parasitic forms include the 'pin' worms of dogs, cats, and humans. More serious infections in man include elephantiasis caused by the worm blocking the lymph system. Many also cause serious damage to plants by piercing the cells and sucking out the contents.

6 Phylum Rotifera

These are the 'wheel animals' whose characteristic feature is a ring of cilia around the head (the 'wheel'). They are tiny freshwater animals important in the plankton as a major food source for other species.

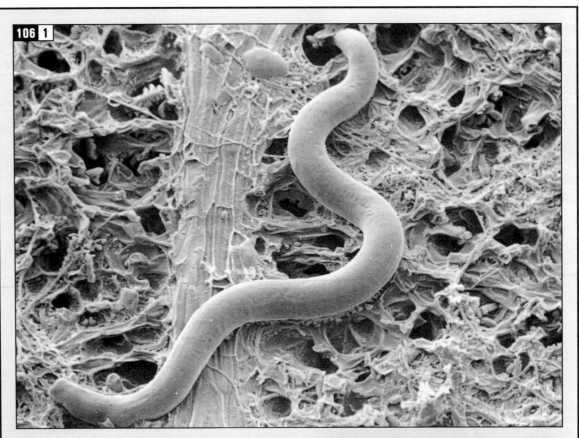

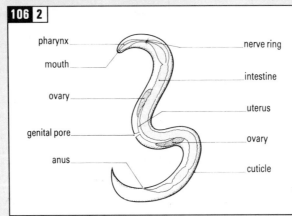

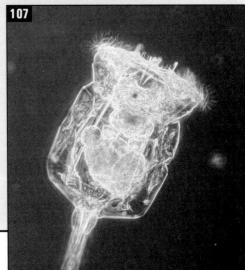

Figure 106
1 A nematode (× 800).
2 Drawing of *Rhabdias bufonis*, a nematode parasitic in the lung of the leopard frog, *Rana pipiens*.

Figure 107
A rotifer, *Brachionus* sp.

Grade Coelomata

Coelomate animals are divided into two series: Protostoma ('first mouths'), in which the first opening to the gut to form during embryonic development becomes the mouth, and the anus forms later; and Deuterostoma ('second mouths'), in which the first opening to form always becomes the anus, and the mouth forms later.

Series Protostoma

7 Phylum Mollusca

The molluscs are a very diverse and successful group of animals. The most unifying feature is their soft, flexible body wall, and little evidence of segmentation. There are seven classes of mollusc, but the most familiar ones belong to one of three groups.

Class Pelecypoda (Bivalvia)
Bivalves include clams, oysters, and mussels. The shell consists of two hinged valves which enclose the body. They are typically burrowers in mud and sand and most are filter feeders, the gills being large and involved in food collecting as well as gas exchange.

Class Gastropoda
These molluscs include snails, slugs, and limpets. Typically they possess a spiral shell into which the animal can withdraw (but in slugs the shell is reduced to a trace). A toothed rasping organ known as a radula is usually used in feeding.

Figure 108
A hypothetical early mollusc. The characteristic molluscan features are shown: a head, foot, and visceral mass covered by the mantle which produces the shell; feathery gills in the mantle cavity; and a mouth with a radula. This early molluscan form gave rise to all present day forms.

Figure 109
A bivalve, the common cockle, *Cardium edule*.

Figure 110
1 Land snail, *Helix* sp. In land forms the mantle cavity is modified as a lung.
2 Scanning electronmicrograph of a radula (× 330). The radula bears rows of chitinous teeth and is used for grazing (scraping algae off rocks) and for cutting larger food materials.

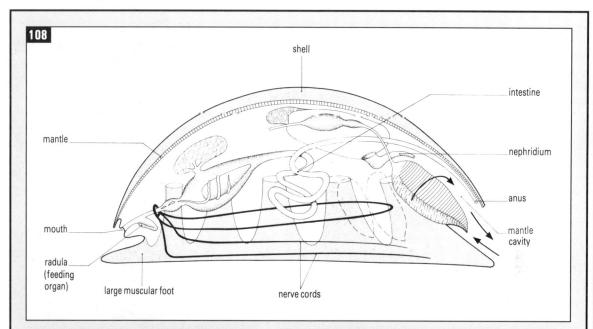

Class Cephalopoda

This group contains the octopus, the squid, and the *Nautilus* (the only living species in which a completely developed shell is found). In other living species the shell is reduced and internal. Cephalopods are adapted for swimming. They are very specialized and reach the largest size of any invertebrate. They catch their prey with 'arms', and have a horny beak and a radula (which is used more as a tongue).

Figure 111

1 *Octopus vulgaris*, crawling.
2 Drawing of the body plan of a cephalopod. Although highly specialized, the cephalopods still retain the characteristic molluscan features. The 'arms' are homologous to the 'foot' of other molluscs.

8 Phylum Annelida

These are the segmented worms. Their body is divided into a series of more or less similar units which are divided internally by septa. They have a closed circulatory system with blood often containing a respiratory pigment.

Figure 112

Body plan of an annelid worm, showing characteristic features.

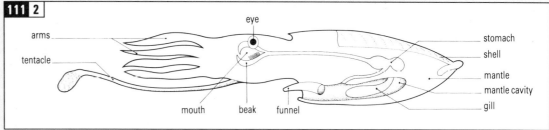

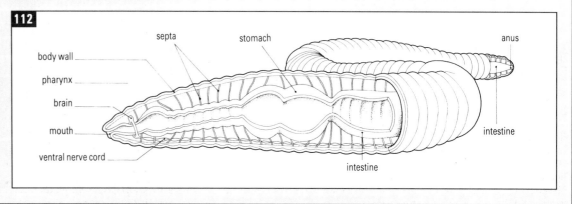

There are four classes of annelid, of which three are described:

Class Polychaeta

The name means 'many bristles': examples are the bristle worms, fan worms, peacock worm, and lugworm. They are very numerous, but rather secretive marine annelids. A characteristic feature is flaplike extensions of the body wall called parapodia, which bear the bristles or setae. The sexes are separate, the release of eggs and sperms being synchronized. Swarming often happens, as this increases the likelihood of fertilization.

Class Oligochaeta

These animals, with 'few bristles', include earthworms, and there are some aquatic forms. They are hermaphrodite animals, with male and female sex organs in each individual. During copulation sperms are exchanged, but fertilization and development take place in a cocoon which is produced by the clitellum.

Class Hirudinea

These are the leeches. Their method of reproduction is similar to that of oligochaetes. Their distinguishing feature is the presence of an anterior and a posterior sucker. Some are free living and carnivorous; others are parasitic and suck the body fluids of animals.

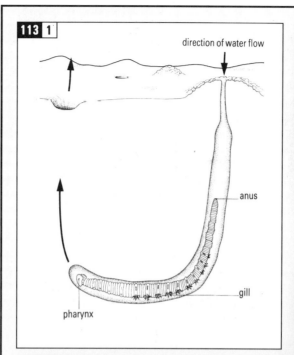

Figure 113

1 A burrowing polychaete, the lugworm, *Arenicola* sp., showing the worm in its burrow. The worm ingests the column of sand on the left through which the water filters. The piles of sand on the surface are castings expelled from the anus.

2 A tube-dwelling polychaete, the peacock worm, *Sabella pavonina*.

Figure 114

Copulating earthworms, *Lumbricus* sp. The clitellum which produces the cocoon can be seen.

Figure 115

Freshwater leech, *Pisicola geometra*, on the tail of a three-spined stickleback, *Gasterosteus aculeatus*, showing the anterior and posterior suckers.

9 Phylum Arthropoda

The arthropods are segmented animals with a rigid, chitinous exoskeleton and jointed legs. During their development the coelom as found in annelids is suppressed and a different cavity called a haemocoel develops. A heart pumps blood into the haemocoel and this bathes the body organs, supplying them with oxygen and nutrients. The blood returns to the heart through pores. This is called an open circulatory system.

The arthropods are the most successful group on earth. Because of their vast diversity the phylum is divided into several large classes (see table 13).

Insects are a terrestrial group although some of them pass through aquatic stages during their life history (for example mosquitoes, mayflies, and dragonflies). They are of immense importance to humans as pollinators, as pests of crops and stored food, and as carriers of disease.

Figure 116
Drawing comparing a true coelom with a haemocoel.

Figure 117
Some representative uniramians. Insects characteristically show a division of the body into head, thorax, and abdomen. The thorax bears three pairs of legs and, if present, one or two pairs of wings.
1   Clouded yellow butterfly, *Colias crocea*.
2   Red ants, *Myrmica rubra*, collecting honeydew from aphids.
3   A mayfly nymph, *Rhithrogena semicolorata*, from a hill stream.
4   Centipede, *Lithobius* sp.
5   A 'cathedral' termite mound, Australia. Its height is approximately 5 m.
6   Grey squirrel flea, *Orchopeas howardi*, amongst squirrel fur.
7   Common black millipede, *Tachypodoiulus niger*, crawling over wood with yellow fungus.

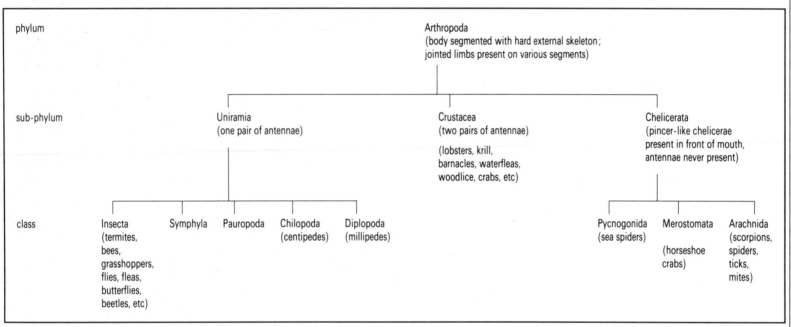

Table 13
A classification of the arthropods (based on Barnes, 1984).

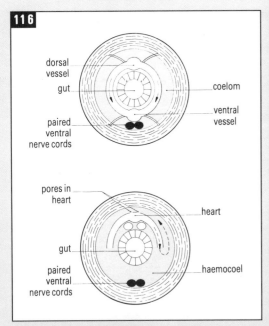

dorsal vessel

gut

coelom

paired ventral nerve cords

ventral vessel

pores in heart

heart

gut

paired ventral nerve cords

haemocoel

116

117 1

117 2

117 3

117 5

117 4

117 6

117 7

Figure 118

Crustaceans show the greatest specialization of appendages among arthropods and are the only ones to have two pairs of antennae on the head. With the exception of woodlice, they are aquatic. Barnacles are sedantary crustaceans, which can be recognized as such by their jointed appendages used for gathering food from the water. Some representative crustaceans:

1 Crab, *Cancer pagurus.*
2 Lobster, *Homarus vulgaris.*
3 Woodlouse, pill bug, *Armadillidium* sp.
4 Water flea, *Daphnia obtusa*, with eggs inside brood pouch and young swimming in surrounding water (× 9).
5 Acorn barnacle, *Balanus balanoides*, feeding under water, .

Figure 119

Some representative chelicerates:

1 Thick-tailed scorpion, *Androctonus* sp.
2 Spider in web, *Araneus diadematus.*
3 Velvet mite, *Acari* sp.
4 Horseshoe crabs, *Limulus polyphemus.*
5 Male sea spider, *Nymphon gracile*, carrying eggs on ovigerous legs.

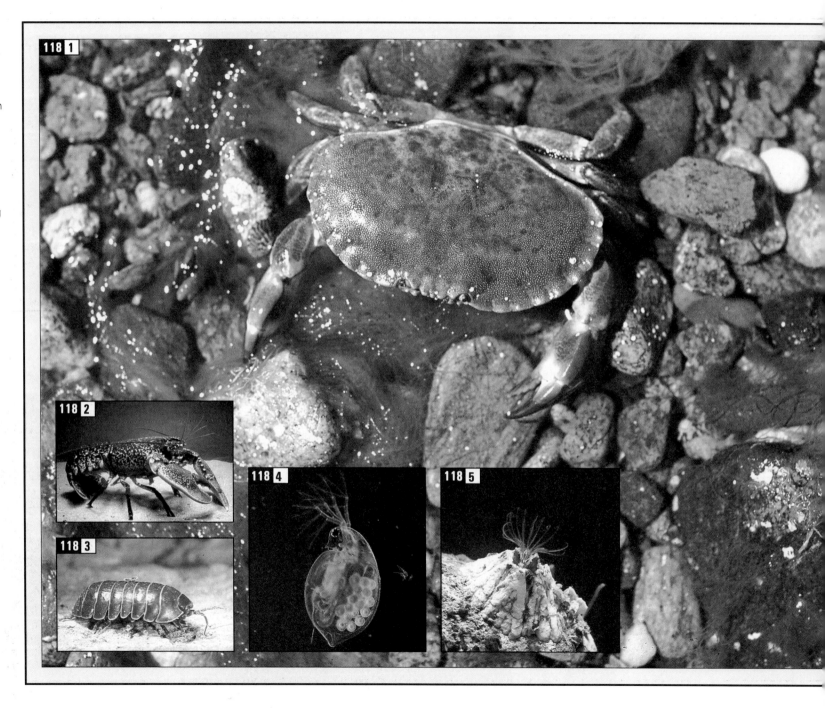

119 1

119 2

119 3

119 5

119 4

Series Deuterostomata

10 Phylum Echinodermata

Adult echinoderms show radial symmetry (see figure 120), but this is a secondary development as the embryos of echinoderms are bilaterally symmetrical. They are an entirely marine group.

There are five classes. An example of each is shown in figure 121.

11 Phylum Chordata

Chordates are distinguished by possessing at some stage of their life cycle:

a dorsal hollow nerve cord
a set of gill slits in the throat
a flexible supporting rod called a notochord
a post-anal tail

Table 14 shows a classification of the chordates.

Figure 120
Body plan showing the characteristic features of echinoderms. The tube feet are part of the water vascular system. They are primarily for walking, but are also used in food collecting. They are extended and withdrawn by alterations in the pressure of the fluid in them.

Figure 121
Some examples of echinoderms:
1 Feather stars (Crinoidea). The majority of crinoids are extinct. They differ from other echinoderms in being attached to a substrate by a stalk and in having their mouths facing upwards.
2 A starfish (Asteroidea), *Asteriase rubens*. The arms are not sharply marked off from the disc.
3 Brittle star (Ophiuroidea), *Ophiothrix fragilis*. The arms are sharply marked off from the disc.
4 A sea urchin (Echinoidea), *Echinus esculentus*. This is cushion-shaped and without arms.
5 A sea cucumber (Holothuroidea). This is sausage-shaped and without arms.

Figure 122
Drawing showing the characteristic features of chordates.

Table 14
A classification of the chordates, based on Young, 1981 and Margulis, 1982.

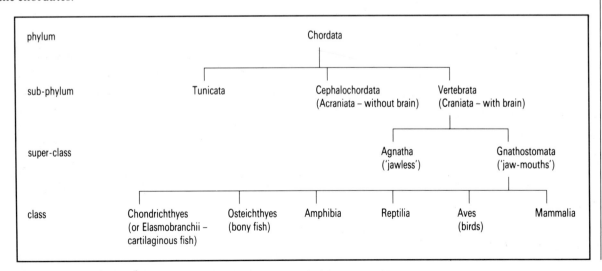

phylum			Chordata			
sub-phylum	Tunicata		Cephalochordata (Acraniata – without brain)	Vertebrata (Craniata – with brain)		
super-class				Agnatha ('jawless')	Gnathostomata ('jaw-mouths')	
class	Chondrichthyes (or Elasmobranchii – cartilaginous fish)	Osteichthyes (bony fish)	Amphibia	Reptilia	Aves (birds)	Mammalia

120

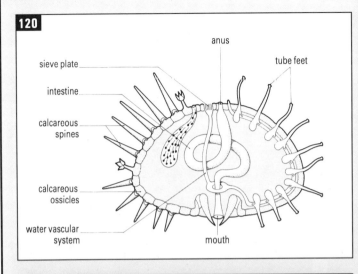

sieve plate

anus

tube feet

intestine

calcareous
spines

calcareous
ossicles

water vascular
system

mouth

121 **1**

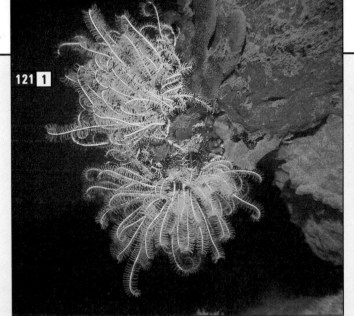

121 **2**

121 **3**

121 **4**

121 **5**

122

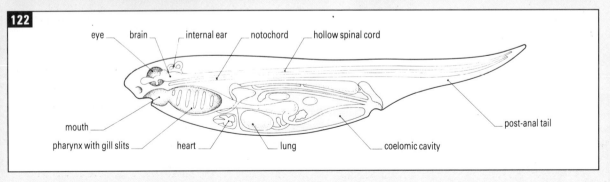

eye   brain   internal ear   notochord   hollow spinal cord

mouth

pharynx with gill slits   heart   lung   coelomic cavity

post-anal tail

The sub-phylum Tunicata consists of sea squirts, and the sub-phylum Cephalochordata consists of only a few marine creatures.

In the sub-phylum Vertebrata (Craniata) as the embryo develops the notochord is replaced by a skeleton of cartilage or bone, which allows strength and flexibility for movement. The super-class Agnatha includes only a few jawless fishes such as the lamprey.

All the remaining vertebrates have biting jaws. The skeleton also has pectoral and pelvic girdles for the attachment of paired fins or limbs. They are in the super-class Gnathostomata. They are divided into six classes, as shown in table 14.

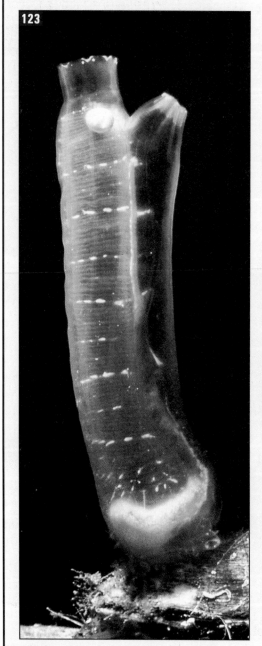

Figure 123
Sea squirt, *Ciona intestinalis*. Chordate characters are present only in the larvae. Adult sea squirts are sessile filter feeders.

Figure 124
Lancelet, *Branchiostoma lanceolatum* (*Amphioxus*). Cephalochordates are swimming and burrowing filter-feeding fish-like animals which display basic chordate organization.

Figure 125
Brook lamprey, *Lampetra planeri*. The jawless fishes (Agnatha) have no paired fins and they feed parasitically on other fish using a sucker mouth.

Classes Chondrichthyes and Osteichthyes

Present day fish occupy two of the classes, according to whether their skeleton is made of cartilage or bone.

Figure 126
Black-tipped shark, *Carcharhinus* sp. (class chondrichthyes). The skeleton is made of cartilage, and they have two sets of paired fins and fine gill slits. This class also includes dogfish, skates and rays.

Figure 127
Horse mackerel, *Trachurus trachurus* (class osteichthyes). The skeleton is made of bone, there are paired fins but the gills are covered by a flap (operculum). Most present day fish belong to this class. It includes coelacanths and lung fishes, which are modern relations of ancient groups, as well as the more familiar fish.

Class Amphibia

The development of a bony skeleton gives land vertebrates an adequately strong and rigid support for their own mass. Amphibians were the first land vertebrates. They have legs and lungs, although the moist skin is largely used for gas exchange. The eggs are laid in moist places or actually in water; and the tadpoles are aquatic, using gills for gas exchange. Adults suffer from desiccation if deprived of water for long.

Class Reptilia

Reptiles are a difficult class to define (see page 14). They are truly terrestrial, with overlapping scales on the skin which prevent water loss, internal fertilization, and eggs with an impermeable covering which are laid on land.

Figure 128
Photographs illustrating some of the characterisitic features of the class amphibia:
1   Male crested newt, *Triturus cristatus.*
2   Common frog, *Rana temporaria.*
3   Frog spawn, *Rana temporaria.*
4   Seven-week-old tadpole of common frog, *Rana temporaria*, with hind legs developing.

Figure 129
Reptiles have no internal means of regulating their body temperature. By suitable behaviour, basking in the sun or sheltering under vegetation, they are able to maintain a remarkably constant level for much of the time. However, this cannot be achieved for a long period, so they survive heat and cold by aestivating in warm countries and hibernating in cold ones. Representatives of the class reptilia:
1   Red-eared turtle, *Pseudemys scripta elegans.*
2   Parachute gecko, *Ptychozoon lionotum.*
3   Southern smooth snake, *Coronella girondica*, female with eggs.
4   Muggers, *Crocodylus palustris.*

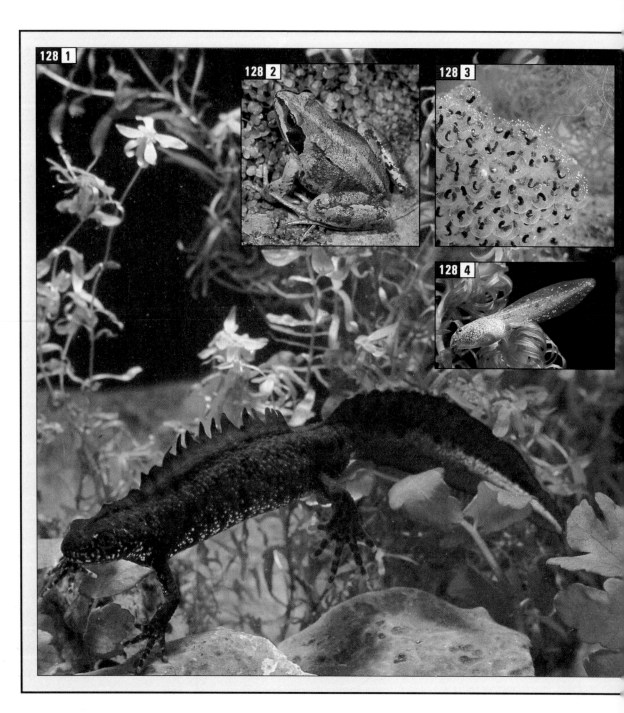

129 1

129 2

129 3

129 4

Class Aves

The birds are often called 'feathered reptiles'. Differences from reptiles are all connected with flight. Bird features are concerned with the need to be both light and powerful. They lack teeth or heavy jaws, and their bones are often tubular with internal strutting and air sacs extending into them. Their high body temperature which, unlike any creature mentioned so far, they can regulate internally, and their rapid heartbeat helps them to achieve the power they need for flight.

Figure 130
Although birds show fairly constant basic features they have a great variety of special features suited to numerous habitats.
1   Barn owl, *Tyto alba*.
2   Rhea, *Rhea americana*.
3   Emperor penguin, *Aptenodytes forsteri*.
4   Swallow-tailed gulls, *Creagrus furcatus*.
5   Sedge warbler, *Acrocephalus schoenobaenus*.
6   Mute swan, *Cygnus olor*.
7   Fairy tern, *Gygis alba monte*.

130 4

130 5

130 6

130 7

Class Mammalia

The superficial feature of mammals is the possession of hair on their bodies. In addition, they nourish their young with milk and have a large brain. There are many other mammalian features, such as a single bone forming the lower jaw and three auditory ossicles in the middle ear, but it is largely their behaviour and their ability to maintain a high body temperature and a constant internal environment that has contributed to their success as land vertebrates.

Figure 131

Some of the features of mammals can be seen in these photographs.

1 Long-eared bat, *Plecotus auretus.*
2 Tiger, *Panthera tigris.*
3 Polar bear, *Thalarctos maritimus.*
4 Vervet monkey, *Cercopithecus aethiops.*
5 Red kangaroo, *Megaleia rufa.*
6 Duck-billed platypus, *Ornithorhynchus anatinus.*

131 4

131 5

131 6

Index